SILVER SISTER

Lillian Ng was born in Singapore as Ng Cheng Chye. Her parents fled their home in JiangShia near ShanTou, a sea port in the Chinese province of Kwangdong, just before the Sino-Japanese wars. Lillian had a traditional Chinese upbringing. As a child she learned the Chinese classics by rote in the Teochew or ChiaoChow dialect, and wrote with a brush pen. When she entered medical college she gave herself the English name of Lillian. She specialised in obstetrics and gynaecology, and practised in London for eight years before coming to Australia in 1972 with her baby amah and her daughter. She now lives in Sydney with her elderly mother and her daughter, and continues to practise as an obstetrician and gynaecologist.

LILLIAN NG

Silver Sister

Published 1994 by Mandarin Australia
a part of Reed Books Australia
22 Salmon Street, Port Melbourne, Victoria 3207
a division of Reed International Books Australia Pty Ltd

Reprinted 1994 (twice), 1995

Copyright © Lillian Ng, 1994

All rights reserved. Without limiting the rights under copyright above, no part of this publication may be reproduced, stored in or introduced into a retrieval system, or transmitted in any form or by any means (electronic, mechanical, photocopying, recording or otherwise), without the prior written permission of both the copyright owner and the publisher.

Typeset in Galliard by Bookset
Printed and bound in Australia by Australian Print Group

National Library of Australia
cataloguing-in-publication data:

Ng, Lillian.
Silver sister.

ISBN 1 86330 379 0

I. Title.

A823.3

This work was assisted by the Australia Council for the Arts, the Federal Government's arts funding and advisory body.

Acknowledgments

I would like to thank Wellington Lee, OBE, OAM, RFD, JP, foundation president of Chinese Chamber of Commerce (Vic); the Australian Chinese Community Association (ACCA) of New South Wales; Belinda Byrne, Julie Pinkham, Adrienne Ralph and Suzannah Macfarlane of Reed Books Australia for all their help, enthusiasm and encouragement; Mark Zocchi of Angus & Robertson Bookworld, organiser of the Angus & Robertson Bookworld Prize; Barbara Brooks, teacher of the WEA creative writing class; and my writing group: Sandy Wagner, Ann Hobson, Lee Carsley, Dorothy Hayes and Kay.

For Wong (Ah) Ngan
baby amah to Jeffrey Tan, Pauline Tan, Patricia Tan,
Beverley Peh-Li Tow and Li-Yu Loh

Contents

Village

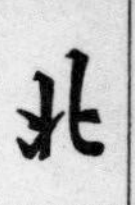

A BALMY SUMMER DAY typical of Sydney in February. A large crowd has gathered in Dixon Street Mall, to welcome the Chinese New Year. Firecrackers explode — pop, crackle, bang — dispelling the bad luck demons. From the shop awnings dangle green lettuces tied with red-packet — good luck money for the dancing lion to retrieve amidst the beatings of drums, gongs and cymbals.

It's the year of the Monkey, 1992. When I first arrived here it was the year of the Pig, 1971. The pig, a symbol of comfort, leisure and plenty, opened the door for me to my adopted country, Australia. I came to help Kim just before the birth of her daughter. Kim had been in my charge since the day she was born. She came to Sydney to study at university, qualified two years ago as a doctor, was involved with a married man and then deserted by him. Baby Suchin was born in the month of the Eighth Moon Festival, on the eighth of October. *Pah*, the Chinese pronunciation of eight, puns with *fah*, meaning to prosper. Eight is a figure much favoured by the Chinese as it stands for good omen, a lucky number. When I see vehicles in Sydney's Chinatown with numberplates 888, or any combination of eight, I know they're personalised plates chosen by their Chinese owners. The Chinese, superstitious as ever, even in this modern country, will avoid the number four at all costs as it is pronounced 'say', meaning death or die.

I do not know my own birth sign, or the year that I was born. My parents never told me — I doubt they knew. I was born in China, in the province of Kwangdong, in a village called Lung Sun: Dragon Hill. My parents did remember that I had arrived in the winter solstice during the political upheaval in which Pu Yi, the last emperor, was ousted. There was no registration of birth, or death, in my village in those days, and so I have no birth certificate. Birthdays — and deaths — are remembered by their association with historical events. For me, accuracy is not important, as long as I have a set of figures for my passport and pension application. So in my passport, my date of birth is the twenty-fourth of November, 1912.

Memories of my childhood: doors that did not close. They were made of light cheap wood, hole-ridden with borers, they creaked and trembled in the wind. My ancestral home was a wooden hut, bare and decrepit, near a large plot of rice fields. The floor was of naked brown earth, the roof thatched leaves which leaked whenever it rained. My sisters and I had fun placing broken urns, cracked bowls, and discarded tin-cans to catch the rain water. Our furniture was makeshift: logs of wood, branches of trees, bundles of twigs tied together to serve as seats or low stools. At night we slept on mats of reed on the floor, our tattered quilted jackets doubled up as blankets. During the day the mats were rolled, fastened and placed against the wall; two wooden crates placed in the centre of the room served as our dining or work tables. A bamboo-slatted partition separated our sleeping quarters from those of our parents, giving them some privacy.

I could not keep count of all my brothers and sisters, nor did I know their names. Papa was known as Wong Lao (Old Wong) and my mother was Wong Ma, but we were called according to our place in the family. I was number eight and hence my name was Ah Pah, meaning eight.

But now I'm known as Silver Sister, a name given to me when I started work at the House of Tang in Canton, when I was fifteen or sixteen. And what's in a name anyway, I say to my friends, for despite my names Ah Pah and Silver — both of which denote wealth and prosperity — I have never been wealthy. I came from a poor family: my father used to line us in a row once a year to count the number of mouths he had to feed at the New Year Festival dinner. I remember there were thirteen of us one year, and it upset him to see so many.

'*Aiyah!* Times are bad, with the flooding and the poor harvest — and yet so many mouths to feed and clothe.' He turned to my mother. 'Why did you give birth to so many live ones, and so many slaves?' And he pointed at my sisters and me. 'Good for nothing slaves, can't help in the field or fight in the war.' He stamped his feet in frustration and sighed. However, the number of my siblings fluctuated from year to year. Two years later there were only five of us left. The silver money my father and brothers earned from farming came in handy for the Chinese New Year, the only time Papa went to shop for cloth for sewing our suits and shoes, and for dried provisions such as sausages, smoked duck and sweetmeats for the New Year Feast. But the important item was strips of red-paper with couplets of good-meaning, written with a brush-pen, and crude prints of the Door

Gods. These were pasted on the doors to keep out bad luck.

On that particular New Year's morning, when I was probably eleven, I woke up with a blood-smeared face, and red stains on my quilt and pants. I sat up and howled, terrified.

'*Aiyah!* What bad luck you bring!' my mother exclaimed. 'The curse on New Year — don't you dare shed tears on such a festive day.' Menses was regarded as dirt, a discard from the mysterious inside of women, an inferior being, the Yin, embodying the undesirable and bad luck.

My big sister taught me to 'ride the horsy'. Once a month, I rolled a piece of rag to wad it across my bottom, securing the ends with a cord or belt tied at the waist. My 'horsy' soaked up the blood with its stale smell. My skin was chafed by the dried cake of clots. The rag was recycled. When the bleeding finished, it was soaked, washed, dried and folded, ready for use at the next period.

'Be careful of drunken men,' Mother warned. 'You could get pregnant once you start "riding the horsy".' I couldn't work out the connection between my 'riding the horsy' and getting pregnant. Mother never discussed such intimate topics which were regarded as taboo, and frowned upon, unmentionable especially in the presence of father and brother. My sisters were just as ignorant as myself.

Mother herself was always pregnant. Female babies were secretly smothered with rags or drowned by dipping their heads in a shallow basin of water even before their first cry.

'Girls are a liability to the family,' Papa always reminded us. 'A losing concern, for they marry out to strangers who demand dowries.'

Every day Papa and my three elder brothers got up at the cock's first crow to work in the rice fields about two *li* away. For farmers like Papa there was no time off from the farm, no annual leave or weekends off. It was work from morning until sunset: tilling the land, planting, reaping, attending to the domestic animals and the vegetable patch or repairing the house.

We woke up even earlier than the men, to help Mother kindle the fire, fetch water from the well, cook breakfast, and knead dough to steam buns as lunch for brothers and Papa. For breakfast the men had a thick gruel or boiled rice with salted fish and salted eggs. We females had to dilute our gruel to a watery consistency and ate it with pickled olives and salted vegetables. Meat and rice were reserved for the males, the superior beings capable of manual work, the income-earners of the family.

Females were fit only for household chores. We sewed and darned, cleaned the place, aired the mats and squashed bedbugs, caught cockroaches to feed the chickens, worms for the ducks, and trapped mice to feed the dogs.

But it was the washing that we enjoyed most. Mother never came with us, too occupied with babies and toddlers. My sisters and I left soon after lunch, for a stream about one *li* behind our house. We took the soiled clothes of Papa and my brothers, and raced each other, laughing and joking, our pigtails flying about. We splashed in the cool, clear water, so clean that the bottom was visible. I liked to climb on the boulders to survey the whole expanse of the stream. Under the rocks dwelt the little sea creatures: silent sea serpent that slithered along the sand, jumping frogs with protruding eyes, and miniature crabs that crawled sideways. I tried to scoop the schools of minute fish but they slipped through my fingers. I was obsessed with round pebbles. One day I dived to the bottom and found a perfect round one, with a central hole which I threaded with a cord to wear round my neck. We swam with our clothes on, and washed them at the same time.

There was no soap. We used the fine sand to rub the dirt and grime off the clothes, and the grease off our bodies. As we lay on the grass in the sun to dry ourselves with our clothes on, we let loose our hair. The mens' clothes, which we spread out on the grass, were crisp and fresh by the time we departed for home at sunset. We sang a moonlight song merrily on our way.

> 'Moon shining bright,
> mirror our night
> olive fragrance
> burn an incense
> for our loved ones
> to give us a son
> Ai – ai – ai – ai yo-oh.
> Ai – ai – ai – ai yo-ho.'

It was a never-ending song, for one of us would continue with the chorus while the others start the stanza again. But as soon as we neared home, we stopped singing. Mother would not approve of it. 'Decent girls don't sing such a song,' she would say. Another taboo.

After sunset, Papa and brothers came home, tired and grumpy. We were the target for their bad moods and temper. Scapegoats. 'Fetch my tea . . . my rice . . . some water.'

Brothers, Papa, men, all were bullies. They slapped our faces if we were slow, or pulled our ears and pinched our arms, our buttocks. They called us 'good-for-nothing slaves' and other names. Mother would always side with the men. I think she was afraid of offending them.

There was no bathroom in our hut. Washing was done by the well just outside the house.

At night we used a wooden bucket as a chamberpot, and the urine collected overnight was used as fertiliser for the fields and vegetable patch. The stench of stale urine, sweat and bad breath saturated our house, mingled with the almond aroma of squashed bedbugs. As for the 'big business', we went to a man-made pond not far from the rice fields. It was full of fat carp that leapt up to catch the excreta in mid-air. We squatted on a platform partitioned with thin walls and broken doors, our feet firmly planted on either side of the hole in the centre of the platform. I loved to bend my head down to watch the hungry fish jump for their food. Some droppings fell into *kangs*, large earthern urns placed near the edge of the pond. Manure-collectors emptied these into wooden buckets and carried them on poles across their shoulders. They also took the night-soil from the pigsty, the compost of waste matter — ashes, bones, feathers — and mud scum and green moss from stagnant parts of the pond. The spill from their buckets as they jogged left a stinking trail that lingered for days.

Our village had only one main street of hard mud, flanked by a row of shops on either side. Our landlord owned the largest shop — an office and a barn for storage of rice, wheat, barley, and dried beans brought in by the farmers. Next was the general store cluttered with goods of every kind, stacked high on shelves: joss sticks, candles, paper money for the deities or ghosts. The medicine-herbalist shop had an eerie atmosphere with bottled reptiles and insects in amongst deer-horns, moulted antlers, long dried penises of mysterious animals, and bundles of dried herbs. Across the street was a temple, were a Taoist priest lived. A tea-house, which operated as a brothel upstairs and a gambling parlour behind, stood next to an inn with a restaurant.

There was no school in our village.

But it was the street itself which came alive at night. Like a stage, well-lit with lanterns, candles and oil-wicks. Vendors laid their wares on sheets on the ground, and clamoured for attention. The dentist exhibited the teeth he had extracted, and sets of dentures for prospective customers to try. The optician bade passers-by to try spectacles, pince-nez and magnifying glasses discarded by previous owners. The charlatan stood with a snake wound round his neck. 'Come and drink the potion of gall bladder in wine. Good for your sex life.' For dramatic effect he stabbed a sharp knife into the snake and squeezed out a small gall bladder into a cup of wine. Desperate men queued to buy the aphrodisiac and drank it there and then. These shows were interspersed with loud shouting and banging of gongs and cymbals. A trained pet monkey, dressed as a warrior in an armour of red and green, performed acrobatics to the delight of children. Quietly, other vendors set up their stalls. The onion crepe man with his portable wok and charcoal stove. The smell of fried onions wafted across the street mixing with the fragrance of roasted chestnuts: 'Come, come, come, buy my delicious onion crepe.' When the crepe man stopped hawking the chestnut vendor started: 'Buy, buy, buy, my roasted fragrant chestnut, special price tonight'.

But the centre of attraction was the storyteller, who narrated his tales partly in verse by beating time with a bamboo castanet. He mimicked his characters: a female high squeaky voice, the hoarse husky tone of an elderly person, or a baritone. His tales were a series, which continued night after night, each episode ending with a cliffhanger. Fragments of classics, mixed with figments of his imagination, with humour and comedy thrown in. The charge was a copper for the duration of burning an incense stick. We never paid any money, for we had none, so we stood at the back of the crowd who sat or squatted on wooden crates. Often we wept at the tragic fate of the heroines. With red and sore eyes, we walked home, fascinated by the tale we'd heard, swinging our lanterns before us. Every night the whole population of the village poured out onto the street to partake its diverse entertainment.

Now, in my one bedroom apartment in Ultimo, Sydney, I sit back on my chair in the evenings, prop up my feet, and watch the heroines of the village storyteller come alive on my colour TV. The videos are taped in Hong Kong and flown in daily. Such serials are often based on history, adapted classics, with Kung Fu, acrobatics and sword fighting for thrill, dramatised with comedy and tragedy. These soapies are in great demand by the Chinese here, who rent them for home entertainment. I often watch the local programs too. There are four channels, and once in a while they even show a movie in Chinese on SBS, but all the other programs are in English. Although I can't understand the dialogue, I enjoy watching the action, expression and body language, which are quite self-explanatory. My favourites are documentaries of the outback and countryside of Australia.

It fascinates me to watch the shearing of sheep and Australian methods of farming: the use of machinery, tractors, piped irrigation, greenhouses of controlled temperatures, and large trucks with cutters for harvesting and collecting the produce, with only one man in command at the wheel, not an animal in sight to do the plowing. I think of my poor Papa and brothers labouring away with bent backs all day planting, plucking, beating the yoked buffalo to till the fields, and carrying buckets of human excreta as manure to fertilise the land, their efforts often coming to nought in adverse weather and conditions.

Late autumn in the village was time for harvest. Papa and elder brothers thrashed the cut sheaves on the ground in front of the house, beating the ears of grain with flails. As for winnowing, we girls cast the flat bamboo baskets to catch the good grain, and saved the chaff for the stuffing of quilts. We helped to measure, weigh and store the grain in jute bags. After counting and marking the sacks, Papa and brothers carried them in baskets on the ends of poles across their shoulders to their landlord. Papa was paid half in silver money and half in rice, with appropriate deductions for renting of the house and rice field. At the start of the farming year, the farmers consulted the storyteller to read the almanac, an annal of forecast of the elements of nature: rise and fall of tide, wax and wane of the moon, rain, sleet and frost. They wanted an auspicious time for planting the next crop. If the predictions were ominous, the farmers' wives made offerings of food and burning of joss-sticks to appease the gods. The Taoist priest donned his long saffron gown, his black tapered cap, and with a bell in one hand and a sword in the other, conducted a ceremony with chantings and prayers to ward off misfortunes.

Winter crept in. The north-west wind from the mountains

was bitterly cold. Every morning the fields were covered in a blanket of mist, and the young plants withered in the frost. In the cold season, Papa planted hardier crops: wheat, taro, tubers, together with fast crops of cabbage, beans, potatoes and peanuts.

Rain. First a drizzle, light and refreshing. But by Ching Ming, the festival of sweeping of the graves, the rain continued non-stop. The hard mud floor of the hut became soft and soggy as the roof leaked. The walls sagged and partly caved in. Then rain poured, drowning all our crops, our domestic animals, swelling the pond and burying the toilets. The carp disappeared. The rice fields were a conglomerate of puddles. The stream overflowed its banks. We sat up all night on our makeshift stools, covering ourselves with the damp quilted jackets. From the summit of Dragon Hill the water eroded the hillside, carrying the silt with it; it splashed from heights as red muddy cascades and roared down to the valley where our village nestled, flooding tracks and the main street. The stream hurried, afloat with carcases of animals and corpses of female infants, and wrecks of huts and furniture.

Mother bawled: 'What have we done wrong to deserve such calamity? Oh Kitchen God, didn't you put in a good word to the Gods of Heavens for us, after all I've smeared your lips thick with honey?'

After a whole week of heavy rain, it suddenly stopped. The sun shone. The intense heat of summer quickly dried up the moisture. But here and there, puddles bred maggots, flies and mosquitoes. Diseases spread. Our two younger brothers succumbed to the vomiting and diarrhoea. We buried the infants, wrapped in rags, in a grave among our ancestors, at the far end of the pigsty.

Then came the famine, and Papa was forced to sell my

two pretty elder sisters to a brothel, and another two to a rich family as slaves or concubines, so that they wouldn't starve. My sisters and I clung together and cried and held on to Mother's hands, we knelt and appealed to our parents not to separate us, but Mother was without any feeling or emotion, stoical, and Papa and brothers finally dragged the sisters away by force. 'You don't want to starve to death, do you?' they shouted.

I wished I could go with them, to have a chance of survival, free of hunger, but nobody chose to buy me, Mother said, because of my eye defect. (My right eyelid droops when I'm tired, and my nose is flat, almost level with my face, and I am short: I stand up to four feet nothing.) Our neighbour, Lee Sao, the only close friend of the family, remarked that I was probably the reincarnation of a toad, and it would be very hard for me to find a husband. My mother often worried about my future and said with a sigh that it would be better if she had stifled my cry as soon as I was born.

But I had helped to earn a few coppers by selling, through Lee Sao, a foot length of my hair to the rich ladies in Canton to pad their chignon. I also sold the thick grey pus from the pox on my arms for the charlatan to innoculate others against the disease of 'sky flower' or small pox, during an epidemic. Many died, but those who survived were riddled with pockmarks on their face for life. I was an exception, my skin unscarred.

The drought continued for a month. The earth cracked, mud split, trees, grass, plants wilted. Animals died from thirst. The water level of the well was very low, we extended the rope to a greater length to tap a little precious water further down. The stream exposed its rock bottom. We could walk from one bank to the opposite.

Mother couldn't produce enough milk to feed the baby

and toddlers, and they cried till they were hoarse, gradually wasting away.

We sucked the juice from the grass roots, weeds, and any wilted plants. Men killed any living animals or insects, and drank their blood. I was covered with sores where maggots crawled, and flies followed me like bees in a hive. My hair thinned out, and my scalp was studded with abcesses. Pot-bellied children sat or stood listless, like lemons on matchstick legs. Occasionally travellers who passed through our village brought fresh fruits and vegetables from other provinces for sale, but these were expensive. Only the rich, like the landlords, could afford to buy them. We rummaged through their garbage, scavenging for the peels they cast away.

Bad luck appeared as a cyclical occurrence of natural disasters — rain, flood, diseases, drought, famine. But the year I started to menstruate, a different kind of disaster struck — war. It was a new threat to us in secluded Lung Sun, where news from other parts of China filtered through by word of mouth as gossip, announcement, propaganda or hearsay. There was no radio and newspapers were unheard of; most of the villagers were illiterate. The various tales told by the village storyteller were our only education.

I remember the first time I heard about wars was from his narration of Sun Tzu, a contemporary of Confucius, who was noted for his writings on the art of war. The storyteller often quoted his wise sayings: 'Know your enemy . . . know yourself . . . and in a hundred battles you'll never be defeated'. A skillful commander was likened to a particular species of snake found only in the Zang Mountains; when it was struck on its head, its tail attacked, when struck on its tail the head attacked, and on its centre both its head and tail attacked . . . And many battles fought were based on Sun Tzu's theory, especially in the Three Kingdoms (AD 220–265), with careful studies of the enemy's terrain, together with the consideration of the state's economy. And the various ploys and tactics engaged such as deception in feigning incapacity, immobility; the use of guides and spies; attacks by inundation or fire, depending on the weather, wind and time; the use of noise on the battlefield, blowing of bugles, beating of gongs and drums; the use of colourful flags and banners, and torches at night — such appeals to the sight and sound were used to guide and unify the troops. And yet the Chinese were conquered by the Manchu who ended the Ming dynasty. The last Ming emperor, having lost the battle, hanged himself on a locust tree at the foot of Jingshan Hill in Peking. The tree is still standing there in Peking to this day, the storyteller emphasised, and I cried on hearing how the Ming princess had died in a suicide-pact with her bridegroom at the wedding ceremony by drinking poisoned wine, to avoid capture by the enemies.

At night while waiting for the storyteller to begin, the crowd discussed the wars: I pricked my ears to pick up the snatches of conversation going on.

'Chinese fighting against Chinese: Kuomintang and Communists . . .'

'A revolution is on; peasants, slaves, workers against landlord, warlord, mandarins . . . There are strikes, riotings, subversive speeches in street corners, public places.'

'What about our Ching emperor, Pu Yi, the revered Son of Heavens? And the Imperial Palace with so many eunuchs, empresses and ladies in waiting?'

'The revolutionary army has taken over, and the inhabitants have disbanded, the eunuchs fled with their preserved gonads!'

More rumours of wars as more people passed through our village.

'A new enemy: myopic Eastern dwarfs, who speak a foreign tongue, have invaded Manchuria, and put Pu Yi on the throne — a puppet kingdom — Manchukuo.'

'Manchurians? The barbarians?'

'The Chinese have joined forces to fight the new enemy.'

'You mean the Communists befriended the Kuomintang?'

'And the soldiers of the enemy have gone on a rampage: burning, looting, killing, raping; shops smashed, farms deserted, mansions broken into, ransacked. Many Communists have gone underground.'

We villagers of Lung Sun, so isolated and sheltered from the rest of the Middle Kingdom, were confused by words such as strikes, revolutions, Communists, Kuomintang, warlords, Sun Yat-sen . . . From then on I half expected to see arrows fly through the air and soldiers with swords and spears to charge in from the mysterious north. At night I lay awake and listened for the sounds of galloping horses, and bugles. When I expressed my fear and concern to my family, my brothers laughed at my ignorance.

'*Aiyah*, nowadays they fight with guns which trigger off bullets which could pierce through the skull and heart from a great distance, and they drop bombs which explode with a loud sound like firecrackers and burn a whole house, razing it to the ground.' Papa sighed. '*Aiyah*, the foreign devils invent such deadly weapons to invade and defeat us Chinese, so the northeners have to evacuate their homes and flee southward.'

'But who are the enemies?' I asked Lee Sao, who seemed to have good first-hand gossip from the bazaar of the village.

But she said: 'Who knows? The Kuomintang and the Communists are Chinese, the Manuchurians look Chinese and speak Chinese and they're all fighting among themselves. The Japanese are the short myopic people, but also can be easily mistaken for Chinese. It's very hard to tell them apart.'

Then came the exodus in groups of families, relatives and friends. The rich with their entourage of slaves and servants, pushing and pulling carts packed with trunks and chests. The masters and mistresses were carried in sedan chairs, the slaves followed on foot, each one carrying bundles, parcels and backpacks, the men with bamboo poles across their shoulders balanced at both ends with baskets of dry provisions. Wet-nurses waddled with babies strapped to their breasts.

Many faltered on the way from exhaustion. The able-bodied men piggy-backed their elderly mothers or grandmothers, who could not walk with their bound feet.

Young mothers with their chains of toddlers, would call out now and again to check that they were all there.

At night they rested. The rich stayed at rooms in the inn, others sheltered under trees by the road, and knocked on doors of farmers for use of facilities. By dawn they were up, eating whatever provisions they had, then hurried on their way. Some were heading to Kweilin, others to Chung King, most went south towards Canton and beyond; others had no set destination, beyond 'the big cities, where it's easy to make a living'.

They left in a cloud of dust. A few would be abandoned along the way: the sick, the weak and the dying; the blind, the maimed, and the simple-minded. They became beggars, wandered aimlessly, bemoaned their fate, but those elderly women with the stumps of useless bound feet had to drag themselves on the ground or crawl on their hands and knees to beg for food. Corpses bobbed in the stream and hung from trees in our once peaceful village. The following day more stragglers arrived. Our main mud street was congested with such processions. They brought news of the advance of the enemies; of their atrocities and destruction. As days went by, the pace of the travellers grew more urgent. Most continued their journey even at night, by lanterns or candlelight.

Lee Sao, our neighbour, came to say goodbye. She was leaving for Canton, to be with her brother Uncle Fatty Lee. Lee Sao had no children and had recently lost her husband; she had been very close to Mother and us girls. We knew we would miss her greatly.

'Take care,' she warned us. 'Hide your silver and dry provisions in little packets, in different places. I hear that the Japanese are gaining ground, taking Manchokou, Shanghai, Nanking. China is in turmoil, civil wars have started, the Communists have gone underground to hide in the mountains, Kuomintang are retreating southward . . . if they should pass through this village, run from your home and hide from their sight. Don't trust any soldiers, they don't hesitate to rob, rape, loot and kill, even kidnap young able-bodied men to be their servants. The Kuomintang leader is General Chiang Kai-shek. They're all from the north, the northerners are tall, and speak a northern dialect. Store as much food as you can.'

I was very sorry to see Lee Sao go, our only helpful friend, our source of information, my mother depended on her for advice and counsel, and comfort when she was bullied by the men. We sobbed and begged her to stay with us. But she assured us she would return as soon as the war was over.

'Remember I still have a house here and all my things . . . and you are my life-long friends,' she told us.

In Lung Sun nothing very exciting eventuated. Once the refugees had departed, life went on as usual. The weather improved, diseases were not as rampant as before, and the dry spell was broken with some rainfall. Papa, three elder brothers and all the farmers resumed work in the rice fields.

But one day came muffled sounds from the distance, sounds which became louder and more distinct; a grating noise on loose stones. Then a column of marching soldiers came into sight, enveloped in clouds of dust and sand. It was the zenith of noon, and most people were indoors. They peeped from behind shut windows, watching the soldiers in grey uniforms and caps as they marched into the village, their bayonets shining in the sun. Their baggage and parcels were borne by a swarm of men, going on before them, dressed in shabbier uniforms. As soon as they reached the main street the column broke up. Soldiers began forcing their way into the locked shops and houses, looting valuables, ignoring loud cries and pleas. They invaded the tea-house and restaurant.

'Bring food and bring plenty of wine for all of us,' they ordered, banging the table, demanding service.

Pigs were slaughtered, chickens killed and speedily plucked. Full of wine, the soldiers became boisterous and rough, wrecking furniture and breaking cups and bowls. Exhausted and drunk, they slept in heaps on the floor.

Mother said they were probably the Kuomintang, retreating south, for they fitted Lee Sao's description of tall stature and speaking northern dialects.

'We have to hide away from the house,' Mother said as she hastily stuffed two packets of peanuts in our quilt jacket pockets. 'You three girls go to the bush at the far end of the pigsty, I'll take Ah Sai with me for he may need my milk. We mustn't stick together in a large group. Keep very quiet, suppress your cough or sneeze. You may have to spend the night there, don't come home until all's quiet for some time, after the soldiers are gone. Be brave.'

We hid all night in the bush behind our empty pigsty; Mother with Ah Sai in a different place from myself and my two younger sisters. Papa and my three brothers were away in the rice fields and hadn't come home.

The night was filled with eerie sounds of crying, screaming, and moaning. It was daylight when I heard noises, from our house, people shouting: 'Nothing here worth taking . . . Let's go.'

And after a long time, I heard our doors creak and flap — the doors that did not close.

My sisters were still fast asleep when Papa came looking for us.

'*Aiyah!* Terrible, terrible . . . they have taken away Ah Tai and Ah Yi by force. I was kicked in the chest trying to stop them.' Papa sobbed. 'Where's your mother?'

'She's with Ah Sai.'

We searched the bush and shrub. Suddenly Papa shouted: '*Aiyah, lai ren ah*'.

Ah Sai was hidden in the vegetable garden, fast asleep, next to Mother who was lying in a pool of congealed blood.

Papa, third brother and myself carried Mother inside the house. She was having a miscarriage.

'They took our two elder sons . . .' Papa cried. 'Only third son left — he was in the toilet at the time, luckily . . .'

Mother, pale, weak and breathless, uttered with great effort to third brother: 'Run . . . to the hills . . . stay alive . . .'

Quietly she bled to death. We stood watching, completely helpless. We heard that in the hills there was an underground resistance force. After third brother had dug a grave and buried Mother, he gathered his quilted jacket and a packet of red beans, pocketed two silver pieces, and bade us goodbye before joining a group of young men to seek refuge in the hills. That was the last I saw of him and when he left I wasn't too sorry to see him go, not the same way I felt about Lee Sao or my sisters when they were sold. I was never close to my elder brothers or Papa, for they, the men, often bullied us, treated us females as inferior creatures to be sneered at and ridiculed, abused and beaten, yet we were expected to serve them, to cook for them and wash their clothes. They held no respect not even for Mother. I'd heard the storyteller refer to women as subordinate to men, and explain how they should obey first their fathers, and after marriage their husbands and later their sons.

Overnight, I assumed the responsibilities of an older sister among the two younger sisters and Ah Sai, the three year old. Papa was in a lot of pain from the kickings and beatings of the soldiers. His chest was bruised, and he breathed with great difficulty.

Our house was a terrible mess. Everything was upside down — stoves, cauldrons, and woks were broken. All our makeshift furniture was scattered, the bamboo partition torn. We scavenged in the pigsty and vegetable patch for anything edible.

We followed Papa to beg by the roadside. He cried out in his rasping voice: 'I cannot bear to see my children starve.' He gave away two younger sisters to passers-by from another province down south. 'Kind "teachers" please feed them,' he sobbed, and on our way home, amidst his coughing bouts, he said: 'Two mouths less to feed. At least they have a chance to survive elsewhere.'

Papa was bedridden for days, delirious with fever. I made a bed for him with planks and mats salvaged from the ruins and came upon his hoard of silver pieces — proceeds from sale of my eldest sister to the brothel during the last famine.

The power of money. I hadn't the occasion to possess or use any silver pieces before, but I'd seen Papa saving them 'for a raining day'. About the only time he bought things with them was before the New Year Festival dinner. These silver pieces gave me the courage to approach the physician-herbalist to help and heal Papa. And the first questions he asked were: 'Have you got a silver for my fee? Have you any *money*?'

I cried my heart out, and implored the physician to save Papa's life.

'Please do your best, he is our only parent.' I knelt on the floor, dragging my youngest brother Ah Sai with me. 'Have pity on us, my brother is barely three, we need our father,' I begged him, tugging at the hem of his gown to press the urgency of the matter.

I presented the one piece of silver to him with both hands, with reverence and hope. 'Please accept this small fee. It's all we've got.'

'How long has he been coughing up blood?' the physician asked, while biting the piece of silver and rubbing its edge to test its authenticity. Father spluttered and spat, seized in a spasm of coughing. He tried to sit up but was too weak. I rushed forward to support him.

'Fetch the spittoon, Ah Sai,' I shouted.

Papa, with great effort, brought up a large lump of red, like a piece of liver. Fumbling weakly in his pocket, he found another silver piece.

'Our last piece. Be of good heart,' he whispered.

The physician pocketed it, this time without testing. He sat by Papa's side and felt Papa's pulse. In a low voice he recited, partly to himself: 'Quick, thready and irregular, typical of internal heat dissipating, and deterioration of a vital organ.' Next he pulled down Papa's lower eyelids, and stared into his irises.

'It's galloping consumption,' he pronounced, standing up and shaking his head sadly.

'Oh no,' I cried. 'Please do all you can. Papa must live. We've nobody else in this world. We cannot afford to lose him.'

Ah Sai was disturbed by my hysteria and sobbed loudly, holding on to my hand and Papa's.

'Come to my shop to collect the herbs,' the physician said. 'Boil the bundle in four bowls of water, condensing to half the amount. He must drink the whole lot tonight.'

He shook his head again.

'Tell us Papa will get better, please, you must . . .' I pleaded for an assurance.

'Well, the herbs will soothe his chest and ease the spasm. And his breathing won't be so laboured after the treatment.'

The physician strutted out of the house without another look at Papa, his long gown flapping in his stride, the pieces of silver jingling in his pocket. Papa drank the herbal extract. We all fell asleep from sheer exhaustion.

One day there was Papa. A skeletal human being, coughing, gasping for air, fighting for life. The next day he was silent, serene; his face drained of colour. He looked remote. Nothing could hurt him now.

For days I had been in despair, alarmed by his protracted coughing and terrified by the appearance of blood in his spit. Now he was dead. A corpse. His last wisp of breath drowned by the herbal drink. Ah Sai and I hugged each other for a long time. I became composed, resigned to Fate.

'You still have me,' I consoled him. 'We're the only flesh and blood ties left in this family. We must depend on each other. But first, we must bury Papa.'

Village

Once a month I buy a stalk of spider orchid, of green, brown and ochre petals, to lay on Ah Yin's grave in Botany Bay, in the eastern suburb of Sydney, a place with good *feng shui* on elevated ground with a view of the sea. This orchid costs me about five dollars, but it was Yin's favourite flower, grown in Malaysia and Singapore, now flown here by Interflora. Ah Yin deserves this little indulgence; she didn't have much luxury in her life, was exploited by her boss and died a tragic death. She was one of my four adopted 'sisters', and had come to Sydney to be close to me, hoping that we would spend our old age together. But it was not her destiny.

I'm glad she had a proper burial; a wake in a funeral parlour, a well-polished wooden coffin, and now lying in a prestigious graveyard, her plot cemented, a marble tombstone etched with a recent photograph of her. I cannot help comparing her burial with that of my Papa's, and I often wonder how I got the strength and the guts to bury Papa in the back of our ancestral home. By force of circumstances, as the Chinese proverb goes, 'when your horse dies you have no choice but to walk'. And at the time I considered it as part of the filial piety or obedience of old China, teaching of Confucius, as often stressed by the storyteller of Lung Sun. So after wiping my hands on my torn and tattered clothes I thought to myself: my duty is done; it is finished, the last scoop of earth has been heaped on the mound that is Papa's grave. The burial is completed, by me, with a little help from Ah Sai. Papa has at last lain down to rest. And now Ah Yin, too, has lain down to rest, out here in this strip of foreign land.

'Life must go on,' I mutter as I bow to a smiling Ah Yin's photograph on her tombstone, as I had muttered to Ah Sai at Papa's grave.

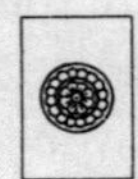

'We must piece the wreck back together. Ah Sai, go look for scraps — leaves, grass, roots, bark of tree — bring them home to me. Don't wander too far away from the house.' Ah Sai, a toddler with snot running down his nose, lean and hungry, cold and dirty, didn't understand what had happened around him in such a short time, or why Mother and Papa had gone to sleep in the earth.

I started to tidy the kitchen, to fix the stove and cauldron, and discovered the two packets of red beans and peanuts hidden in the earth near the wall. How long had it been hidden there? A few weeks or months? It was the end of the dry season. Summer. The wind stirred, a thin film of dust rose and settled, the sun was setting and soon it would be dark. The water level in the well was very low after the drought. I had difficulty drawing it, only managed to get a small amount after a few attempts.

I handed Ah Sai a few grains of red beans. 'Here is your dinner. Put one at a time in your mouth, let your saliva wet it for a long time, chew well before you swallow.'

He nodded; he seemed to understand hunger and the need of satiation, even at his age, he who was still breast-fed only a few days ago. With the water, I boiled a gruel over a slow flame with the sprigs of weeds chopped into tiny pieces, stirred to disperse the bits of mud and grains of sand stuck to the roots.

I promised Ah Sai that the next day we would venture

out again to scout and search for food for survival. But without Papa, we were at a loss. He had been our guide and instructor, our decision-maker. With Lee Sao gone, there was nobody we could turn to for help; my parents and elder brothers were very strict and controlled us with a cane rod. We were only allowed to go to the stream for washing clothes, and to the storyteller at night, as a group, and were warned time and again not to speak to strangers, not to linger at neighbours' homes. 'Girls should be confined to their home, and are not to display their presence publicly, in a wanton or ostentatious manner.' We were threatened with beatings if they should ever catch us doing so, and then our only freedom, our visits to the street market to be entertained by the storyteller, would be stopped. Our mother hardly ventured out of the house.

There was no one we knew in the neighbourhood, and the houses were far apart, separated by the rice fields. Weak and hungry, Ah Sai and I had only the last few peanuts to eat since our house had been ransacked, and all food looted. We found our way to the main street. But the price of food was exorbitant. I had only two pieces of silver left.

'Let's try buying a cooked meal,' I suggested to Ah Sai and went to the tea-house and the restaurant. But the place was under repair.

'Follow the crowd,' the carpenter advised. 'They're heading for the charity kitchen where you can get a meal for a copper.'

Vagabonds, refugees, everybody was heading south. Compelled by hunger, Ah Sai and I, equipped with a tin can each, followed the crowd. We made this journey with fear, as we had never left our village before.

'Usually takes four or five hours to get there if you walk briskly,' a traveller said. 'But if you're hungry and weak it's best to break your journey, rest at night, and continue the next morning as the charity kitchen is opened once a day, in late morning.'

'At this time of wars, people still operate charity meals?' I asked.

'It's sponsored by a wealthy warlord out to win favour and support from the people to be on his side in the wars.'

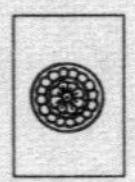

How can I compare such a charity set-up with those in Sydney? The Vincent de Paul? The Sydney City Mission? The Smith Family? It wasn't a feed for the destitute, or the winos, or the confused drug addicts; or even the Christmas lunch of turkey and other festive fare served up for the old folks without homes. Maybe there are charity soup kitchens which I haven't heard of, but Australia is a land of plenty, nobody is starving — except those who want to be slim — no one should, and help is available from the welfare services. The most comparable example is the news I see on television of famine in the African countries; the Ethiopians, Somali, women with drooped dried up breasts, reduced to skin and bones, children with pot-belly, listless, haloed with flies, old men too weak to move. But then rescue comes in helicopters, army trucks bring sacks of dry provisions.

In Lung Sun in my time there was no Red Cross, no helicopter. Help didn't come to us, we had to walk there, me and Ah Sai, and the hundreds of refugees.

I was so anxious, so worried that we would get lost, or would get there too late when the food was finished; yet it was a trip filled with the hope of a meal in our deep agony of hunger, hoping for a mirage with the promise of spring, an oasis with water mirrored in the desert of dryness.

When dusk fell, it was hard to see. The road was very uneven, full of pits and holes. Everybody was forced to rest. We slept under a blanket of darkness, with no moon or stars. Ah Sai and I huddled together for warmth and comfort.

We watched the sun rise. The people around us packed their mats, quilts and blankets, and gathered their possessions to resume the journey. My shoes, the new pair for the New Year, were wearing thin. Ah Sai was barefooted, and limping after a branch had stabbed into his foot.

'Be careful, watch where you're walking, you must learn to take care of yourself, now.'

We soon came to a forked road. Most of the crowd took the smaller loose-stoned track to the right. A traveller pointed to the direction of the track.

'To Fok Sun, the Ancestral Temple, the charity kitchen.'

'Hurry up,' I said to Ah Sai, as I gave him the last peanut to chew. 'We don't want to miss out.'

The road led slightly uphill, to a wooded seclusion. The Ancestral Temple came into view, shaded by tall pine trees, with a stream running behind it. We rushed forward, and fell on the edge of the stream, scooping up the clear water with our tin cans. We had not drunk for a whole day and night! It felt good to wet my dry lips, crusted and cracked, and I splashed water on my face, my arms, legs, stinging the sores and ulcers. Ah Sai too enjoyed his bath in the stream. Beggars were everywhere. The blind, the maimed, the diseased, the lepers, the deformed, harelips and cleft palate, pock-marks, the simpletons. Some with babies strapped on slings. Children, dirty and in rags, infested with sores and lice. Those with bound feet were at a disadvantage, they couldn't walk or push, and were left out in the queue. Holding tin cans, cracked bowls, bark of trees, large lotus leaves, they cried out to the passing crowd attending the Temple for prayers.

'Have a good heart.'

'Save a life.'

'May you be rewarded with longevity and prosperity.'

'Help a poor soul . . . do a good deed.'

I listened to their phrases, and taught Ah Sai to recite them to beg for alms. We needed a copper each for the meal.

The kitchen was at the back of the Temple, in an annexe, beyond the courtyard with a pool with a stone serpent and a turtle. Inside the Temple were gigantic statues of eighteen lohans in bright colours, on either side of the altars with incense-urns and candles. The crowd outside the charity kitchen was restless, people were pushing and jostling. Two bald-headed monks with burn-scars on their scalps, in long saffron robes, ordered the crowd to form two queues. At times they had to use force to rearrange the disorderly mass.

'Queue up, queue up, don't fight, there is enough for everybody. Only one serving each. Anyone caught cheating will not be given a meal. Please follow our rules.'

At the tenth hour sharp, the doors of the charity kitchen were thrown open. The two monks came to the threshold to control the queues. Two strong men stood on stools, one on each side of the two enormous cauldrons. Fragrant steam rose from the cauldrons when the huge wooden lids were removed, and the two strong men, their sleeves rolled up, stirred the bubbling contents with a thick wooden ladle.

Everyone held out a copper to drop into the collecting tins of the monks, and the queues separated into two, one for each cauldron. Ah Sai was ahead of me in the same queue.

'When you get yours, wait for me outside by the pool with the stone serpent,' I told him.

Our tin cans were filled to the brim. Piping hot thick gruel of wheat, with beans and traces of lotus seeds and mushroom. A vegetarian meal.

I sat with Ah Sai on the stones by the gate of the Temple, cupping the hot tins in our hands. Carefully we lifted them to our mouths, sipping a little, tasting with our lips, licking with tongues made insensitive by thick coats of fur, trying not to burn our lips.

'Lick it carefully, little by little,' I advised Ah Sai who was very anxious to eat, and scalded his tongue in the process. 'Have patience, wait till it gets cooler.'

We blew and puffed at the contents, and by small sips, licks, sucks, we got used to the hot meal, and slowly drank the thick starchy porridge. With relish we licked our containers clean, turning them upside down to tip the last morsel, last droplet onto our tongues. It was the first substantial meal I'd had for weeks. I could feel it gushing down my throat into the stomach, which contracted in appreciation. A pang of warmth and satiation rose in me, as my energy returned.

The Chinese have a saying, which the storyteller would recite with a reassuring nod of his head whenever the heroes or heroines were in a seemingly hopeless situation. 'Heavens don't point a dead-end route to man.' No matter how desperate one is, there's always a glimmer of hope. And it was in that moment of contentment, filled with the warmth of a good meal, that I spotted our old neighbour Lee Sao, who had left Lung Sun for Canton before the invasion of the soldiers. She was among the crowd coming away from the Temple, presumbly after offering prayers at the altars.

'Lee Sao, Lee Sao!' I shouted after her, waving my tin.

She turned around, scanned the faces in the throng and saw me.

'*Aiyah*, Ah Pah.' And as she came closer: 'Is this Ah Sai?'

'*Aiyah*, Lee Sao.' I burst out crying. 'Only the two of us left, Mother and Papa died and my brothers they —'

'I heard all about you, I went back to Lung Sun to look for you, what a terrible tragedy.'

'We're homeless and begging.'

'Ah Pah,' she came up close and spoke softly, 'I've a suggestion . . . How old are you now?'

'I don't really know.'

'Let me think back — you were born the year the emperor was ousted.' And she counted on her fingers. 'Yes, you must be fourteen now. How would you like to join a "sisterhood"?'

'I need somewhere to live and food to eat.'

'Yes, and you'll have all that plus an income as well, working as a domestic servant.'

'Oh yes, yes, quick, Lee Sao, please quickly help me to arrange. I'm willing to join any "hood" as long as I can have somewhere to live and food to eat, and not be separated from Ah Sai.'

I was cold, hungry and destitute, alone with little Ah Sai, what would I not be willing to do for a roof over our heads and a bowl of rice? What choice did I have?

'I've just come to Fok Sun to arrange for my niece Ah Han and her two girlfriends to form a "sisterhood", before they leave for Canton to start their jobs. It might be a good idea if you join them and make a foursome.'

'Canton? I don't know anyone in Canton. And what about Ah Sai and how we get there?'

'My brother Uncle Fatty Lee will help you to get a job. Canton is a big city, full of people, with lots of families who need domestic help and are willing to pay wages. Ah Sai can stay with Uncle Fatty Lee and perhaps even work as an apprentice in some trade. You won't have trouble getting jobs there. In fact, Ah Han and her two friends already have jobs lined up by Uncle Fatty Lee, and with good families too.'

The prospect of having a place to stay, a meal, and money, filled me with happiness and relief. I was so excited, I didn't even bother to ask Lee Sao what a 'sisterhood' involved. Instead I burst out with many other questions: When do we leave? How do we get there? Do we go on foot (like the refugees) and how long does it take? Do I meet the girls today? Do we start our journey tonight? Or tomorrow?

Lee Sao said: 'I better explain about the "sisterhood" first. It's taking a solemn vow of celibacy, a *sor hei* or "comb-up", with the three girls whom you'll treat like your own sisters, help to look after each other in sickness or in times of difficulty and in old age.'

I looked puzzled, not understanding any of it. I'd never heard the storyteller refer to such vows of celibacy in his tales, except in his episode of Yang Kwei Fei, the favourite concubine of the last of the Tang emperors, XuanZhong, when Buddhism was spreading from India to China, from China to Japan and Korea. The storyteller narrated how women who vowed to become Buddhist nuns spent their lives in the seclusion of nunneries, and had their heads shaved bald and wore long shapeless grey gowns.

'Do I have to shave my head and live in a nunnery?'

'No. You will take an oath before the image of Kuan Yin,

the goddess of mercy, to swear that you will not get married, and that you'll accept Ah Han, Ah Yin and Ah Fong as your adopted "sisters",' Lee Sao explained slowly. 'And those who have taken such vows, grow their hair long, plait it in pigtails or chignon, wear white tunics and black pants as a mark of modesty, not making themselves fashionable to attract men. Do you understand? You will not have a chance to beget children of your own, and your "sisters" will also be your friends and companions for life, just like members of your own family.'

I had never liked the idea of bearing children, having witnessed many times my own mother's suffering during childbirth, and eventually her death after a miscarriage. The thought of not having any intimate relationship with men appealed to me too, after the years of bad treatment from my elder brothers and Papa.

'Yes, I understand,' I replied, but without much conviction.

'You're best suited for this, Ah Pah, as it's not easy for you to get married with your defective eyelid and your looks.' Lee Sao looked sympathetic. 'No matchmaker would recommend you for marriage without any dowry to offer, no families wanted to buy you for a slave and not even the brothel would buy you — remember your mother tried to sell you some months ago and was unsuccessful?'

'To take a vow and not be confined to seclusion?' I was still confused.

'*Aiyah*, you listen to too many stories. This is a different kind of "sisterhood", very widely practised south of Canton in the Pearl River delta of Samshui. The girls are free to choose the domestic jobs they like, free to leave, not tied down, you're not sold as a slave, not owned by anyone, not confined to any nunnery. And you'll have a group of "sisters" to turn to for support.'

I knew I could trust Lee Sao, who had been a friend of the family for many years even before I was born. She had helped us in the past with her advice and counselling, and had wide knowledge of the events in the country, so I looked at her with tears in my eyes. 'Lee Sao, I'm placing our lives and future in your hands.'

'I urge you to go home, collect whatever you want to take with you, and come back here tomorrow after your charity meal. You will meet the other three girls, the "sisterhood" ceremony will start at noon and at four in the afternoon depart by the fire wagon to Canton. You'll get there before dark.' She added: 'Look clean and presentable, wash your hair, for it is a "comb-up" ceremony — a religious vow.'

'Same time same place, here tomorrow, Lee Sao. Ah Sai, let's go home and pack.'

And I raced him all the way from Fok Sun to Lung Sun. I removed my threadbare shoes and ran barefoot back to the dilapidated house where I and my siblings had been born and raised. Now quiet, and in ruins, it didn't seem like a home anymore, for with the passing of Papa we'd lost all that the ancestral house stood for. All that was familiar, that was intimate, that was habitual, had departed; gone too was the sound of laughter, the chatter of men returning from the rice fields, the quarrels of the parents, the shouting of elder brothers, the giggles of silly sisters, and the shrill cry of a new-born babe. Now there was only silence as the house peeled away, layer by layer, tier by tier, our makeshift furniture soaked by flood water, trampled upon, destroyed by soldiers and looters; members of family torn apart by death and diseases, seized by army, sold for silver, given to strangers. Too much had happened while we lived in this house. I was relieved to be able to move away from it, to distance myself from so much tragedy, to erase such nightmares from my sleep.

We rummaged through the piles of rags, quilts and utensils. I patched and darned our tunics, jackets and pants, folded layers of padding for our shoes. During these months of starvation I had missed 'riding the horsy', for I had no periods.

That night, our last night in Lung Sun, we both hardly slept, anxiously waiting for morning to come. Before dawn Ah Sai and I were dressed in the suits we had sewn for the Chinese New Year, with outside pockets for coppers, and an inner pocket for the piece of silver, and I wrapped our jackets and shoes in slings, which we strapped across our chests.

'Hang on to me tightly, so we won't be separated in the crowd,' I told Ah Sai. 'And don't forget the tin can for the charity meal — our last.'

To save our shoes for the ceremony, we walked barefoot, avoiding the pits and holes and loose stones, tracing our way along the same track we'd taken the day before, holding on to each other's hands. We drank the refreshing water from the running stream behind the Temple, and washed our faces, feet and hair. I plaited my pigtail using the stream reflection for a mirror.

Again at ten sharp, we joined the queue for the charity meal. Not long after we had finished eating, Lee Sao came to look for us.

'Come to the nunnery,' she said. We followed her, making our way through the throng, to another annexe on the opposite side of the kitchen.

Lee Sao knocked firmly and, without waiting, pushed open the simple wooden doors: a new set of doors that admitted me to a new life. We entered by stepping over a raised threshold — a deterrent for the bad demons which couldn't negotiate something raised — a strong fume of burning incense, the fragrance of sandalwood, greeted us, amidst a constant sound of tock-tock-tock.

'Ay-ni-to-fa.' Lee Sao raised her clasped hands in supplication when a young nun, robed in a long dull grey gown came forward. Another, older nun stood at an ornately carved altar table, beating a large red wooden 'fish' with a stick, tock-tock-tock, while chanting prayers. Although they wore grey scarves as headgear, I could see their hair was shaven, at the nape of the neck.

'Come and meet your "sisters".' Lee Sao had to push Ah Sai and me forward, for we were both shy and embarrassed to be in such a place and meeting strangers.

'Ah Han, my niece, is the oldest, eighteen; Ah Yin seventeen, and Ah Fong sixteen.'

I smiled and nodded to each and all. The girls were neatly dressed, in floral printed tunic and pants, their hair plaited in pigtails with red string, and all wore new cloth shoes.

I could see the resemblance between Ah Han and Lee Sao. They were the same height, about five feet tall, and had the same shape of face: triangular, with a pointed chin, like the frontal view of a horse. Maybe they're reincarnation of horses, like I'm supposed to be that of a toad, I thought. Ah Han seemed to have read my thoughts, and twitched her nose and mouth, an attempt at a weak sneer or smile. Ah Han's two pigtails were the longest, hanging down to her waist, and when she looked at me her slit-like eyes narrowed as if she had invisible blinkers. The one I warmed to most was Ah Yin, petite like me. She smiled, her face was round like an apple, brightened with two deep dimples, and her eyes followed Ah Sai who by now had hidden behind me, with keen interest. Her sister, Ah Fong, looked very much like her, minus the dimples. Tall and slender, she reminded me of the bamboo pole which my father used to balance two wicker baskets for transporting chickens.

I was fascinated by everyone in this room — especially the nuns in grey robes, just like the characters in the storyteller's tale. I wondered if they possessed magical powers, by sheer effort of their continuous devotion and chanting of Buddhist script, and I envied them somewhat, in their detachment from the outside world of wars, famine, looting and sufferings. I wondered what qualifications one needed to be admitted to a nunnery. To my reckoning, at least, one must be able to read, for the older nun had a book laid out in front of her on the altar table from which she chanted according to the rhythm of the tock-tock-tock. I wished I, too, could learn to read, as I'd heard the storyteller say that 'amongst the leaves of books there's gold' to be found — metaphorically speaking, of course. I concluded that the nun could not have come from Lung Sun, where no school existed.

My thoughts were interrupted by the older nun's announcement: 'It's the auspicious hour, let us begin the ceremony. Each girl is to light a joss-stick, kneel before Kuan Yin, the goddess of mercy, and repeat after me.'

Lee Sao beckoned us girls to go forward towards the foot of a large statue of a lady standing on a lotus plant: Kuan Yin, smiling down on us, a string of beads dangling from her right hand. I knelt next to Ah Yin and, holding my lit joss-stick, bowed to the image in reverence.

We repeated the vow of 'comb-up' or *sor-hei*.

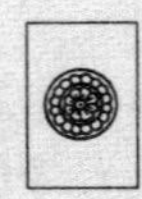

Not long ago I took another vow, a vow of allegiance to become a citizen of Australia. The simple ceremony was held in an office of the Immigration Department in Sydney, conducted by a young Australian man, and in the background was a large coloured photograph of the Queen of England with a diamond tiara on her head. I thought of the coincidence in taking another oath in front of another woman figure. But this vow was uttered in English, and although I repeated it word-for-word after the young man, parrot style, I couldn't understand what I had mumbled in my incoherent English. Through Kim's interpretation I have an idea that I'm obliged to perform the civic duties expected of a law-abiding citizen, as illustrated in the television advertisements: to vote at an election, and do the 'right thing' by throwing garbage in a bin. But after this ceremony I was rewarded with a certificate, documentary evidence of my prestigious citizenship which opens a whole new world to me, a world of legality and status.

The sisterhood vow had no such recording on paper. It was a matter of trust, and of conformity to a dress and hair code, a moral obligation to earn a wage, to save for our old age, a responsibility for our sisters' welfare, and a promise of non-involvement in any other relationship, especially marriage.

So in Cantonese, we repeated the vow after the nun. 'We swear to remain celibate for life, and loyal and true to each other; to seek a wage-earning employment and save our earnings for times of need and our old age. We swear to grow our hair long and plait it in a pigtail or knot it up, wear sober clothes — white tunics and black pants. We swear to be "sisters" of a bond stronger than own blood sisters.'

Then we got up, and planted our joss-sticks in the incense urns packed high with ashes. We stood before the statue of Kuan Yin, while the nun passed a comb through our hair in a gesture symbolic of our vow.

Meanwhile, Lee Sao, after laying out her offerings of flowers and fruits, took Ah Sai away to a corner to burn paper offerings and light candles and oil-wicks, for a small fee, a donation to the nunnery.

The ceremony performed, we greeted each other as 'sister' and Ah Sai became a little brother to four sisters. A meal was laid out for us in the next room. It was the first time Ah Sai and I had ever sat down at a proper table for a meal in our lives. There were four dishes, all vegetables, and a pea and mushroom soup.

Ah Sai dug his chopsticks into his bowl of food searching for morsels of meat. 'I want my fish, I want my fish,' he started his tantrums, having had enough of vegetables in the last few meals.

'Stop complaining and eat up the food, you should be thankful you get something to eat at all, after starving and chewing raw red beans and boiled grass roots,' I shouted, and I pinched his ears and his arms in a fit of temper, and he bawled louder.

My new sisters were appalled at my behaviour, and Ah Yin rushed over to embrace Ah Sai, protecting him from my assault.

Lee Sao persuaded him to eat, promising that when we got to Canton we might have eggs and sausages with Uncle Fatty Lee, and perhaps even a fish.

'Here all ingredients used are vegetables; mushroom,

beans, grains, tofu and its skin: bean curd. I've lived here since my parents disappeared, so I know,' said Ah Yin. She and her sister Ah Fong had been abandoned by their parents at the nunnery.

'Even the charity meals are vegetarian. No meat,' I said.

'Because the teaching of Buddhism is against the killing of lives, so they spare animals by avoiding them in food.' The older nun who had come to top up our rice-bowls added: 'By sparing lives, one gains merits and will be reincarnated in a more superior form in next life.'

'What is a more superior form?'

'Certainly not into peasant family like us,' I said, patting Ah Sai on his head, as a gesture of repentance for losing my temper.

'Someone born into a rich family, with father in high position, like mandarins, merchants or scholars,' Ah Han answered.

'They will form sisterhood, like us?' asked Ah Yin.

'*Aiyah*, they'll be matched with men of equal wealth and high position, and they'll be the ones to employ the domestic servants . . .' Ah Fong sounded annoyed with her sister's naivety.

We laughed and joked and talked while we ate and stuffed ourselves to bursting point.

'Now all you girls and Ah Sai are now like a family; Ah Han is big sister, the leader, and all of you will have to obey and follow her instructions,' Lee Sao told us. 'Ah Han, it's your duty to look after your younger sisters and brother. Soon you'll be leaving in the fire-wagon, have your money ready to pay as you enter the carriage. Hold on to each other, one behind the other, don't be separated or you'll lose each other. And when you reach Canton, Ah Han look out for Uncle Fatty Lee, he will be waiting for you on platform eight. Your jobs have been arranged, except for Ah Pah and Ah Sai because they're last minute additions.'

We left the nunnery soon after the meal, having said goodbye to the two nuns, and walked on with our parcels slung across our chests, Lee Sao leading the way. The station was very crowded, and she was not able to get close to the platform where we would board the train. She was pushed further and further away from us by the growing crowd. She shouted after us: 'Ask Uncle Fatty Lee to send a message to assure me of your safe arrival. Push your way, get as close to the edge of the platform as possible, be aggressive, or you'll miss the train.'

We stood in line, Ah Han the eldest first, and myself last, with Ah Sai in between me and Ah Yin. I could feel my heart pounding away in my chest with the excitement of going away to a new place, a new life. In Canton I would find a home and food, and an income of silver pieces. There was nothing here to hold me back, though I knew I would never forget my place of birth and the passing away of my parents and so many brothers and sisters. These things were etched in my memories, nobody could take them away from me, not even the passage of time. Ah Sai stood bewildered, tightly clutching my hand as he watched the children gathered there with their families. He had never seen such a crowd before. We waited patiently, while all around us the crowd milled, talked, spat, ate. Children cried. Mothers looking for missing infants called out names: 'Little Piglet, come back at once.' 'Small Dog, stop howling or I'll spank you.' 'Big Cow, don't pull your sister's plait.'

Boys were nicknamed after animals to fool the bad demons who might become jealous if the male infants were too handsome and take their lives away. Girls didn't matter, their lives were cheap.

Some fifteen years later in Singapore I hear the same names again, amongst the cousins of a family where I work. Their wet-nurses call out to them when it is time for feeding: 'Dog-number-three, Cow-dung, Big Buffalo', and their names stick in my mind, a reminder of how superstitious the Chinese are, even transplanted in another country, another climate. And later Dog-number-three graduated as dentist, Cow-dung worked as an aeronautical engineer, and Big Buffalo is now a grandfather, and I'm too embarrassed to call them by their ridiculous nicknames whenever I meet them on their visits to Sydney.

The fire-wagon was an extremely impressive sight. We heard the sounds first, the 'chug-a-chung-chung' and a shrill whistle, then we saw black smoke rings spouting from a red chimney at the head of the wagon. Its eyes were two dazzling bright round lights. Its green body had big windows of glass and doors that closed. It rushed into the station, wreathed in smoke. Abruptly it screeched and jerked to a halt, sending the passengers crashing onto each other. A conductor in khaki uniform shouted: 'Chung Sun' through a loudspeaker shaped like a large trumpet.

The doors opened, one from each carriage. Passengers from inside fought to get off, while those on the platform elbowed their way in. Ah Han had mounted on the step, handing the fare to the conductor for the five of us. We followed close behind her. It was the first trip for all of us on a fire-wagon.

'Look at the seats, all solid wood and so well polished,' I said.

Han settled in the first carriage, and we all sat on a long wooden bench facing a similar one opposite. Across the aisle was the same arrangement. The seats were quickly taken. Families came with their parcels, trunks, shoulder poles of baskets. Others with their fowl-pens, piglets, some balanced on their heads; pots and pans and water jars and urns. Many spoke a dialect we had never heard.

'From the north,' Ah Han said.

Old folks who couldn't search for seats sat on the floor, which was also of wooden slats. Soon there was not even standing room left. It was so crammed that Ah Sai had to sit on my lap.

The station conductor gave a signal with his flag and whistle. The doors closed. The fire-wagon roared. We felt ourselves moving forward. People who sat or stood close to the windows were still talking to those on the platform, clutching their hands, last-minute farewells.

I caught glimpses of the landscape as we moved — tilled land, rice farms, deserted houses, dry brown land, a patch of blue sky. Then the fire-wagon gathered strength and ran faster and faster. The talking eased off. Ah Sai fell asleep. The air was stifling and stunk of bad breath and poultry droppings. The sound of snoring, in various tones, filled the carriage. Fong later complained of a numbness in her right shoulder where I had leaned when I dozed off.

I was jostled out of my dream by a screeching sound. The fire-wagon had pulled to a stop. A hamlet. Few people got off and more got in. Vendors came to the windows to sell their wares. Ah Han, who sat closest to the window, bought a hot bun and an ice-stick of red bean each, the cost a copper per head.

Doors shut again. Landscape flew past, more rice farms, run-down houses, monotonous rumblings of the fire-wagon. Then gradually the landscape changed. Rows of two-storeyed houses, streets with people, rickshaws, sedan-chairs, pedal cycles. Marketplaces with stalls. Backyards with fowls, dogs, clothes on bamboo poles flapping in the wind. Shop houses with signs: words in ideograms. Ah Han, who had learned to read, pointed them out to us: 'A goldsmith.' 'Noodle shop.' 'Barber shop.'

Most shops displayed their wares. Cake shop had trays of cakes freshly baked. Butchers hung their carcasses on hooks, dripping with blood. Street stalls and push-carts were piled high with wares. Itinerant hawkers, pedal cycles, ringing bells, tooting horns, rickshaw-pullers shouting 'Lend me your light, "teacher", lend me your light', their legs bulging with veins, muscles taut, skin calloused, a towel thrown over the shoulder. A city throbbing with men, women and children. Dogs and vagabonds scavenged at garbage piles and smartly-dressed women carried parasols to shade them from the sunlight. Strange faces, strange city, big metropolis, the rich mixed with the poor.

The station was cavernous. There were many platforms, numbered and with names of destinations which only Ah Han could read. The fire-wagon sensed it was home, whimpered and died.

'We get off here, platform eight,' Ah Han cried. 'Look, there's Uncle Fatty Lee.'

I recognised him from his visits to Lee Sao. He still looked the same, fat and shirtless, with arms akimbo, trousers tied with a sash around his protruding tummy. We had no hand luggage, only a sling each strapped across our chests. Ah

Han led the way, and we followed in the same order as before, holding on to each other.

'You remember Ah Pah and her brother Ah Sai?' Ah Han started.

'Yes of course.' But he was more interested in Ah Sai. 'And how old are you, little one?'

We addressed Uncle Fatty Lee respectfully, as we had been taught to show good manners to our elders.

'Stay close to each other, be careful in big city, full of crooks, don't trust any strangers,' he advised. 'Come to my place for a meal first, I have rice and sausages and eggs, and then I'll take you to the girls' home where you'll stay for the night. Ah Sai can rough it out with me. Tomorrow I'll come for you three, to take you to your places of work. As for Ah Pah and Ah Sai, I'll scout for something tomorrow. No shortage of jobs here, as long as you're willing to work.'

Uncle Fatty Lee's quarters were one of the many attachments outside a mansion, leaning from a high wall. His place was partitioned with cardboard; a roof of canvas rested on bamboo poles. There was sheet for a curtain at the entrance. Cooking was done on the kerb of the road, on a brazier filled with burning charcoal. Ah Han helped him boil rice, which we ate topped with beaten eggs and sausages. It was a very welcome meal after our long trip. We laughed and chatted and Uncle Fatty Lee briefed us about work in Canton.

That night we slept on mats on the wooden floor of the girls' home in a large room where the girls or boarders slept at night. During the day it was a classroom for teaching handicraft.

'It's the home of a rich widow who uses it as a boarding

house for young girls waiting to start domestic jobs,' Uncle Fatty Lee explained.

Many girls would only go there during the day, to learn a craft from the widow as well as helping her with the house chores. There were many such homes in Canton.

Canton

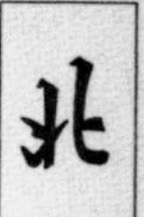

IT TAKES ME TWENTY minutes to walk from my unit in Ultimo to Kim's apartment in Kent Street, Sydney. On the way I always stop at the entrance to the Chinese Gardens, which reminds me of the Garden of Eternal Tranquility in the House of Tang. I linger to admire the set of red doors with brass knockers at the entrance. Once I heard from my neighbour, Mrs Chin, who read in the Chinese newspapers, that Sydney has become the 'sister' city of Canton, now known as Kuangzhou. I still don't quite understand what it means. How can a place, a town or a city, have a sister or a brother? Do they mean there's some resemblance in its climate, its planning or its topography? And is that why they built the Chinese Gardens in the Darling Harbour complex, to clinch the relationship?

In Canton, Uncle Fatty Lee and I spent hours looking for another set of doors — the entrance to my place of work. We walked around three sides of a huge complex, with much panting and sweating. Finally we found it, the main entrance of the mansion, guarded by two huge doors. They were about eight feet high by four feet wide, lacquered black, and studded with rows of brass knobs with two large brass rings for knockers. Spellbound, I stood at the bottom of a flight of four broad stone steps, flanked on either side by a stone lion with a ball inside its open mouth.

'I should have remembered that the entry to these big houses is usually in the north-south axis, positioned according to the *feng shui* of the location, instead of searching from east to west!' Uncle Fatty Lee muttered. 'Let's move on, we haven't got all day.'

'Coming, coming.' I tore myself away, excited at the thought that soon I would be within those doors, behind that tall brick wall and fence of trees and shrubs, living amongst the hidden rich.

I followed Uncle Fatty Lee to a side gate, not far to the right of the main entrance.

'Don't think they're going to open the big doors for us,' he told me. 'They only open for distinguished guests, mandarins and officials, carried in sedan chairs.'

A gaunt figure appeared from a hut next to the side gate. He had a thick mane of unkempt hair. 'Looking for someone?' he asked, picking his nose with his little finger, his palm cupped over his mouth.

'Hey, hey, brother.' Uncle Fatty Lee bowed and edged closer to him. 'Today I've come with the new servant girl to work for your Tai Tai, as arranged with Tang Ma, the chief housekeeper . . .'

The gatekeeper shook his head, showering tiny white

flakes of dandruff, and looked the other way. 'I've no word or instructions from Tang Ma.' As he spoke, air hissed from a gap in his upper lip. Through the defect poked his yellow nicotine-stained teeth and I saw his harelip. Harelip and cleft palate were common features in beggars at the Ancestral Temple.

'Hey, hey, brother . . .' Uncle Fatty Lee fumbled for his belt, and loosened three coppers. In those days, the copper coins had a hole in the middle and were strung on a straw or a cord. The gatekeeper accepted them with a sneer, and tossed back his thick mop of hair.

'Wait here, I'll go fetch Tang Ma,' he said. He disappeared up a long winding path, shaking his mane as he strutted along. A woman stood quietly at the threshold of the hut with a baby at her breast, her face pitted deeply with pockmarks. Like the skin of an orange.

'Match for each other, harelips and pockmarks,' Uncle Fatty Lee remarked after she had retreated.

The sun was high, birds chirped while seeking shelter from the harsh heat of noon. It was well past midday. Tired, hungry and thirsty, I sat on the tree stump and rearranged the padding on my cloth shoes, this time tying them securely with a plaited rag on each foot.

Uncle Fatty Lee had taken three days to find me this job. He was selective, anxious to secure me the right one. He had declined a few offers which he thought unsuitable.

'This job is the right one for you,' he had announced with excitement after arranging it with a lady servant at the marketplace. 'Suitable for someone young with no experience, you'll be a handmaid to a very wealthy mistress in a mansion: the House of Tang.'

No interview was required. Salary as negotiated by Uncle

Fatty Lee was four pieces of silver per month. Accommodation, food and clothing provided. And salary would be doubled at the New Year, plus a bonus — lots of red-packet money. And to think that Papa had sold third sister to the brothel for only four pieces of silver — sixteen years old, and worth only four silvers!

Uncle Fatty Lee added: 'She specifically asks for a "comb-up" or *sor hei* like you.'

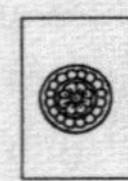

All these years I have believed that a 'comb-up' dressed in black and white, with a long pigtail, had immunity against violation by men, some signal or sign in the manner of dress and appearance saying 'hands off.' And all along I felt safe, as if somehow that vow taken in the presence of Kuan Yin protected me. But last month I heard on the radio that, in a South American country, some nuns had been raped in the convent, their holy place of worship and retreat, nuns in their black and white habits, manifesting to the world their devotion and marriage to the Church, and celibate by choice. What sacrilege!

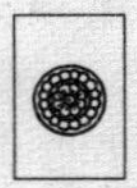

Early that morning, Uncle Fatty Lee had come to the girls' home to take me to start my new job.

'Wear the clean tunic you washed yesterday,' he told me. 'Bundle your personal things inside the quilt and carry it as a hand parcel. A good impression on your first day is very important. Rich people are fussy about cleanliness and neatness. I hope they'll give me a generous commission for introducing you. Then I can take things easy for a while. My old bones are aching.' He hammered his shoulder muscles with clenched fists. 'Pad your shoes well and thick, we have a long walk ahead of us.' We were going to Xi Guan, a district west of the bend of the Pearl River. Now the river is known as Zhu Jiang.

Two days before I had followed him on another long walk, with my three sisters, to the district of Xiao Bai, just outside the city wall in the northern part of Canton, a residential area for people of high rank in the military or government service. My sisters were disappointed that they were not employed by the same family, though they weren't far from each other. Ah Han started work as an assistant cook in the home of a military official, Ah Yin secured a job as a seamstress in the house of a wealthy Mandarin. And Ah Fong took up the post of washer-woman in a house three doors from Ah Yin.

In those days in Canton, as long as one was willing and not fussy, jobs were readily available. Even Ah Sai was accepted by a carpentry workshop as a general hand; he received no wage, but was given free board and lodging. He was only three and a half, but tall for his age, and he passed as a five year old. The boss was a pal of Uncle Fatty Lee's. So, knowing that Ah Sai had secured a place to sleep and rice to eat, I could start my new job with an unburdened heart.

After a long time the gaunt gatekeeper reappeared, followed by a middle-aged woman dressed in an indigo blue pyjama suit, with her hair swept back in a chignon.

Uncle Fatty Lee rushed forward to greet her, 'Tang Ma,

you're well? Hey, hey, this is the servant girl for Tai Tai I mentioned to you the other day.'

'Oh, thank you for your trouble, Uncle Fatty Lee,' and Tang Ma slipped two pieces of silver into his hand.

'No, no.' Uncle Fatty Lee waved both hands in protest, with false modesty, demurring as a gesture of courtesy. The gatekeeper watched with a smirk on his face widening the gash on his upper lip.

'Please accept, it is instructed by Tai Tai.'

Uncle Fatty Lee grinned from ear to ear. 'Thank you, Tang Ma.'

'She will be allowed home on the second day of the New Year Festival, if you would like to come and collect her by the side gate here.'

'Is the New Year soon?' I asked.

'*Aiyah*, it's only the middle of the year now. New Year is another six months away.'

'Six months! I won't be able to see Uncle Fatty Lee, my three sisters and my little brother Ah Sai for six months! I can't leave Ah Sai in that factory for half a year without visiting him.'

'It's the rule of the House of Tang, servants are allowed out or home only once a year. It's the same with most big houses of good repute, you can't be allowed out whenever you like. If you're not happy with the rule you may quit right now.'

Uncle Fatty Lee quickly stepped forward. 'Sorry, Tang Ma. You must excuse her, she's from the country. Of course she'll stay, just that she's not familiar with the rule.' Turning to me, Uncle Fatty Lee said: 'Don't worry about Ah Sai. I visit his boss every day, I work there sometimes too, and I'll keep an eye on him. Six months will soon pass. I'll come for you early on the second day of the New Year. In the meantime, devote yourself to your work, be diligent, listen to the advice and follow the instructions of Tang Ma. Behave yourself in the big House of Tang, have good manners, be honest and truthful. And be polite, speak only when you're spoken to.' And with that, he went on his way.

'Follow me,' said Tang Ma.

I turned back to gaze at the tall brick wall and fence of trees and shrubs that separated us in the House of Tang from the city of Canton. I felt cut-off, walled in, with only a patch of sky up high for a view. And for six months I was to be confined to this place!

I began to wonder whether I had made the right choice, whether I should run now after Uncle Fatty Lee and ask him to find me another job. I worried about how my sisters would cope, each confined to her own place of work among strangers; Ah Yin and Ah Fong, the two blood sisters, separated for six months too? But I was afraid of offending Uncle Fatty Lee, and of making him 'lose face' to Tang Ma by refusing the job he had secured for me. So I decided to give it a trial.

'How can I communicate with Uncle Fatty Lee or my sisters or brother?' I asked Tang Ma.

'You can write a note.'

'I can neither read nor write.'

Tang Ma said: 'I meet Uncle Fatty Lee in the bazaar now and again, if there's any message you would like to send to him you can tell me. And if there's any exciting news regarding your brother or sisters I'm sure he'll let me know.'

'How is that you are allowed out to the bazaar and I'm not?'

'Because I'm the chief housekeeper, I'm in charge of all the servants and slaves, about forty in all, in the House of Tang, I'm also in charge of the necessary purchase for the household. I sometimes take Ho Ma with me, she's number two in charge, we both have been here for a very long time,' and with some hesitation she went on, 'about half a century, for I came and worked here since I was five, and I was in charge of Master when he started attending school.'

I looked at her, and compared her with my mother and Lee Sao, the only other two grown-up women I'd known. Of course I didn't know how old my mother had been, she whose birth and death went unregistered. She never celebrated her birthdays, it was not the habit of poor people like us to do so, and women in those days married young, by the age of fourteen or fifteen. They were labelled as old maids if still unmarried by twenty. I reckon my mother must have had at least sixteen pregnancies, not counting the miscarriages, and when she died she was probably only about thirty-five years old, at most. Yet compared to Tang Ma she had looked ancient, haggard, with parched skin, thin sunken cheeks, eyes rimmed with black shadows, sores festering on her ashen grey lips, her hair shaggy, wiry and speckled white with lice. Lee Sao, her contemporary, was more robust and younger-looking. But I could never have guessed Tang Ma's age, her face was 'full and overspilling' — a Chinese description of someone who has surplus — well-fed and well-padded, her eyes flashed with life, her cheeks were rosy. She towered above me by a head, and though she assumed a stern and authoritative attitude, I felt she might be quite approachable, even amicable.

We trod in silence along a winding path that led from the side gate through a round wooden arch, the start of a long stretch of covered walkways bound by wooden balustrades painted in red. But it was the floor that I appreciated most — such even and level floor, cool with glazed porcelain tiles, a balm to my aching tired feet in their tattered shoes. And

I admired Tang Ma's thick strong cotton pyjama suit and the shoes on her big feet. How I longed for the luxury of a new pair of hand-stitched calico shoes with corded straps and thick quilted pads for soles. By the time we reached the end of the complex, the servants' living quarters, I was so exhausted that I was on the point of collapse. Tang Ma's voice appeared faint, as if fading away, tailing into the distance: 'The washroom for females is at the back of the servants' quarters . . . in the central atrium is the kitchen, and on each side or wing, are rooms partitioned with bamboo screens. The east wing is for male servants, the west for female, even the walkways are designated, west for female, east for men . . .'

North, east, south, west . . . my head was spinning . . . I felt myself falling . . . Then a jumble of voices. A pungent smell of strong ammonia assailed my nostrils and jolted me back to life. I was lying on a mat on a wooden couch in the servants' room. Tang Ma had brought a bowl of hot soup with wheat noodle to revive me.

Sometimes when I doze off in my chair, I dream of that first day, and my introduction to the House of Tang. In my dreams I glide along endless walkways. Through archways I glimpse courtyards as spacious as a whole rice field. Each courtyard is separated by a row of buildings with a central atrium and two wings of rooms. The first courtyard is cobbled, and serves as a reception area with six red sedan chairs complete with matching canopy and curtain. Potted plants of cumquat and bonsai with gnarled and knotted trunks adorn the buildings.

I glide on to my favourite place — the Garden of Eternal Tranquility, landscaped with ponds of lotus leaves and silent carp under a red crescent bridge. A pavilion with a curved roof of green tiles sits on elevated ground. In the pavilion, a zither rests on a stone table with four stools.

The residence of the Old Lord and Ancient Mistress stands between the Garden of Eternal Tranquility and a perfumed garden filled with flowers: carnations, azalias, camellias, gladioli, chrysanthemums, jasmine and orchids in hot houses. Rose bushes, hundreds of them, in shades of red, purple, yellow and white. Each hue exudes a scent so fragrant, so delicate, so individual, and so foreign to me, a peasant, used to the smell of farm land where excreta is used as fertiliser. Now I savour the bouquet of the rich. Drunk with colour, sight and scent, visions of girls swim before me, girls running, screaming, laughing, their pigtails with coloured ribbons flapping, silk dresses rustling, like pictures distorted by ripples on a pond. Women dressed like Tang Ma, netting butterflies, pushing ivory swings into the air, spinning a merry-go-round with horses bobbing up and down, flying kites with eyes and two long tails on a very fine long string. A playground for the children of the wealthy.

I instinctively feel for the pebble hung round my neck with a fine gold chain. The stone pendant is the memento of my playground, that stream with boulders from where I used to dive and wash our clothes and cavort with my sisters. The hard smooth texture of the cold pebble invariably wakes me up.

'A house with forty servants! Is there enough work here to engage forty servants?'

'Don't ask about work, just attend to your own duties. It's rude to mind other people's business. First rule is to be polite, address older fellow workers as uncle or auntie, and younger ones as brother or sister, greet them good morning, and enquire whether they've already eaten rice. The six sedan-chair bearers and six gardeners, each one attending to a courtyard, they're all married and their families live in an outhouse at the back of the servants' quarters. Then there are the chefs, four of them to cater for the needs of four individual bosses: the Old Lord, Ancient Mistress, Master and Tai Tai. We servants eat their leftovers. Ancient Mistress now has two younger slaves to attend her. Tai Tai has six daughters, each with a nanny in charge. I was one of eight slaves when Ancient Mistress married, the other five, for two of them died, now do general cleaning, washing, tidying, sweeping, then seamstresses also double up as washing and ironing women. Tai Tai herself used to have four slaves, you're replacing one of them. The Old Lord and Master have their own personal men servants, and there's Yang Lao, the accountant, Wu Laosi, the scholar who tutors the daughters of Tai Tai, and another tutor who teaches them music and singing, and a calligrapher and artist; these you address as "teachers", and there's the gatekeeper and his family . . .'

'So there are four bosses: the Old Lord, Ancient Mistress, Master and Tai Tai.'

'The actual boss is Tai Tai. Her husband is Master, but he's not very interested in the running of the household. His mother is the Ancient Mistress, and the Old Lord is Master's grandfather. Grasp all that?'

'Three generations under one roof.'

'Master has three brothers, but they're all living overseas, having gone to study, married local women and settled down there. They returned at various times, but their *feng kwei* wives are not used to our local way of lives. He has two aunties who are married. Huh.' She sighed. 'Once the girls are married they belong to their husbands' families, and are seldom allowed to return home, except on very special occasions.'

I wondered how I would ever remember who was who in this enormous household. But Tang Ma was speaking again.

'Before I take you to the Ancient Mistress and Tai Tai, you must bathe, wash and cut your hair, rid yourself of lice, and wear decent clothes and shoes,' she said, eyeing me with disapproval. 'And that parcel of yours must be burnt.'

'No!' I cried, hugging the parcel. 'These are my only possessions.'

'Tai Tai insists with all new servants.' And Tang Ma snatched my parcel from me. 'You must bathe with pomelo leaves to banish bad luck and step over a brazier of fire for purification, pray to the god of the hearth — the Kitchen God — to ward off bad demons, before you enter the House of Tang. These are my instructions.'

I was still pleading with Tang Ma not to cut my hair when we reached the washroom.

'Take off your clothes,' Tang Ma ordered. 'I'll burn them with the parcel in the incinerator. Come, Ho Ma, give me a hand. She's a strong girl I can't cope with her struggles.'

Another woman appeared, stouter and taller than Tang Ma. She was wearing a blue indigo pyjama suit like Tang Ma and her hair was done in a chignon. Together, ignoring my pleas and screams, they peeled off my rags and threw them outside the room. Two men carried a wooden bucket of steaming water into the washroom.

'No men allowed!' I screamed to stop them from entering. 'I'm a "comb-up".' I cowered in a corner of the washroom while they emptied the bucket into a large urn on the floor.

'Huh, what's so special about you?' they growled as they left.

Tang Ma poured pails of the hot water with pomelo leaves over me, while Ha Ma soaped and scrubbed me with a dried marrow.

'Stop, it hurts,' I sobbed. Fresh blood oozed as the scabs came off my sores and abscesses.

'*Aiyah*, you don't know how lucky you are to get into the House of Tang. Everyone here must be clean and neat,' Ho Ma said.

Tang Ma wrapped me in a large cloth and said: 'Now your head must be shaved. Ho Ma, go fetch the barber.'

'No, no,' I sobbed. 'I'm a "comb-up", I must have hair.'

'Hair will grow again, better and stronger. Your head is full of abscesses, shaving will help them dry and heal faster.'

The two women pinned me down between them as the barber went to work.

Finally the barber said: 'This is the best I can do, with scalp so bumpy and lumpy, I can't get it any shorter.'

'See, you still have about an inch or so left.' Tang Ma held a shining brass plate in front of me.

I saw my reflection. 'Is this me? I look like a street urchin, one of those beggars outside the Ancestral Temple.'

For the first time in my life I realised how ugly I was. One of my eyelids drooped, my nose was squashed, the bridge very flat, I had small, beady eyes, and many teeth missing. And I now realised why nobody had wanted to buy me, not even the brothel, and why they chose my sisters instead for they had large round eyes, long eyelashes, wide open eyelids, high noses, small even teeth, pleasant shape of face, lovely to look at. And I threw the brass plate away, frightened at my own image, disgusted with my ugly self.

'My front teeth. I lost my two teeth,' I shouted.

'*Aiyah*, your teeth are rotten anyway. We'll get you a set of dentures tomorrow.'

A seamstress was summoned, and after taking my measurements, she said to Ho Ma: '*Aiyah*, she is of the same height as Ah Lan the ironing woman who left last month. I still have a few of her suits. No need to sew.' And Ho Ma followed her out to fetch the outfit for me.

Dressed in my new crisp white tunic and black pants, and wearing new black cloth shoes, I went with Tang Ma to make offerings to the Kitchen God.

'Tai Tai instructs that you be called "Silver" to replace Gold, one of her four slave girls. The other three are called Jade, Pearl and Ruby.'

So I became Silver Wong or Silver Sister, an address of respect, or just Ah Silver, a friendlier term . . .

I retained my own surname, because I was not a slave, not sold to the family. Slaves were bought by the House, and didn't earn a wage; they adopted the surname of their boss and were considered as part of the household, a chattel. A 'comb-up' like me worked as a domestic servant, for wages. I was not tied down to the boss's family. Although there was no written contract regarding salary, condition and kind of work, agreement was by mutual consent. Employment could be terminated immediately in case of any dissatisfaction or disagreement. Such was the autonomy and power of a wage-earner.

I met Tai Tai that afternoon, when Tang Ma took me to

the 'games' room in the central atrium of Tai Tai's residence, the row of buildings between the children's playground and the perfumed garden.

'Tai Tai plays eight rounds of *mah-jong* after her siesta every afternoon,' Tang Ma explained on the way. 'Lunch at twelve, nap for two hours, and then the challenge of the game.'

'Playing with birds — the sparrow, "*mah-jong*?" I was puzzled.

'*Aiyah*, you country bumpkin — it's "sparrow" the game, gambling with chips and tiles.'

The farmers in my village crouched on the ground to gamble with dice behind the tea-house at the New Year festival. I had never heard of anyone playing the 'sparrow' or *mah-jong*.

Before we entered Tang Ma said: 'Tai Tai is the one dressed in green, be quiet, we mustn't distract the players from the game.'

There were four ladies. One was dressed in light green among three others in striking colours of purple, orange and yellow. The lady in green fitted the description of a heroine as told by the village storyteller: 'A snow-white oval face, the forehead covered scantily by a curved black fringe, her fine brows arched like bridges over a pair of almond eyes, an unobtrusive nose perched above her pouting mouth with cherry lips. From her earlobes dangled sparkling gold earrings set with jade green as broccoli, and her hair falls like a dark cascade loosely knotted at the nape of her white swan neck; her chignon secured by ornamental gold hairpins with fluttering seed pearls'.

The four ladies were seated at each side of a square table, all concentrating on a row of tiles. Behind Tai Tai stood three young girls, all dressed in floral print tunics, their hair plaited in twin pigtails. They smiled at Tang Ma and stared at me.

Tai Tai suddenly shouted, lifting her head, her gold hairpins glittering. 'It's my game, my game. Ha, ha, full house all same colour, full score. Each to pay me six silvers and four coppers.' The other three ladies moaned and grumbled, pushing their tiles away in disappointment.

'The game is finished, we've just completed the North wind,' Tai Tai announced to the three girls standing behind her. 'Pearl, go fetch the guests' servants, and Ruby to warn the sedan-chair bearers to take the guests home. Jade to bring the snack.'

Tang Ma pushed me forward. 'Tai Tai, your new servant girl Silver is here to pay her respects.'

I kowtowed to Tai Tai. She grinned, and a row of gold teeth gleamed. What a good place to keep her assets, I thought, and she could show them off anytime. Then she spoke, in a cheerful voice, soothing like fresh water tinkling from a spring.

'*Aiyah*, you've brought me good luck, Ah Silver. I've won twenty pieces of silver today.'

And always, after that, Tai Tai insisted that I stand behind her at her *mah-jong* table as her mascot, while the three slaves attended to her other needs. Daily I watched the game over her shoulder, noting the tactics and the strategy of winning big stakes. I even learned a few ideograms and the cardinal points from the *mah-jong* tiles.

Tang Ma had briefed me on my duties. I was to stay with Tai Tai at all times, for she had bound feet shod in three-inch 'golden lotus' and was barely able to walk. She needed support day and night.

I slept in the antechamber of Tai Tai's bedroom, as she needed me to fetch the chamberpot. The three slaves were often called away at night to serve the Master, Tai Tai's husband, in the east wing of the building. My bed was of polished wood, well varnished, about two feet high, resting on four wooden bun legs. It was laid with a finely-woven mat covered with a light silk quilted blanket, with a bolster placed at the end of the bed. My pillow was of ceramic, shaped like an oblong box; a mosquito net was suspended within my reach above my bed. It took me a few nights to get used to such luxuries; for the first fifteen years of my life, I had slept on the floor. I would lie awake feeling the soft silk, the smooth polished wood, just to assure myself that I wasn't dreaming.

I woke up very early each morning, even before the cock's crow, to use the washroom in the servants' quarters. The latrines were wooden huts, segregated for male and female, and of the bucket system, reached by climbing two steps to squat on a wooden platform; but here no fish jumped for joy for its food in mid-air, only a swarm of big black flies buzzing away as the bomb fell thud onto the accumulated excreta at the bottom of the bucket. And the stench was so foul and powerful that I pinched my nose so as not to smell it, and now and then gulped air quickly through my mouth, like a diver surfacing for breath.

Most servants were up early and gathered in the courtyard to sit on low square bamboo stools. Everyone came: Tang Ma, Ho Ma, the seamstresses, washing and ironing ladies, cooks, the sedan-chair bearers' wives, the gardeners' wives, and the six nannies. They were grouped in pairs, combing and plaiting each other's hair — they all had waist-length black hair. I said 'good morning' politely to Tang Ma, Ho Ma, and the others, and sat on a bamboo stool between Tang Ma and Ho Ma to help them in their hairdressing, handing them their combs, brass plate mirrors, cords to tie their pigtails, and pins for their chignons from their portable beauty-cases which were discarded biscuit tins. But it was really a social gathering, an occasion for exchanging gossip, stories and information. At first I just listened, but later, when I got more familiar, I joined in with my own queries and contributions.

The gossip would start with enquiries about Gold.

'Tang Ma, how was Gold when you visited her yesterday?'

'Huh! Very depressed. She's getting very bulky, and has swollen feet. The baby is due in another three months. Ho Ma, have you passed word around about a new *naima* for the baby?'

'Tai Tai wishes to interview the applicants first, so I have to be very selective, and keep the list short.'

'*Aiyah*, did you hear that the fortune-teller Tai Tai consulted last week predicted the baby will be a boy?'

'In that case Gold will have a chance to return to the House of Tang.'

'She will be promoted to a concubine.'

'She's much better looking than Tai Tai, and younger, only twenty-one.'

'Tai Tai must be thirty.'

Ho Ma concluded: 'Gold is the prettiest of the four slave girls and Tai Tai is jealous and afraid she may become Master's concubine if she gives birth to a boy. That's why she's been sent to the nunnery. I'm sure she'll not be back if it's a boy.'

'Are you comfortable in your new bed, Ah Silver?' Tang Ma asked me, by way of diverting the small talk away from Gold.

'Oh I'm getting used to it, such lovely furniture and silk and mosquito net.'

'Are you used to the noise?' One of the chefs turned around and asked me.

'*Aiyah*, you mean the noise in the night made by Master?'

'Master is not the only noisy person around here, is he?'

And the servants looked meaningfully at each other.

I was often awakened by Master's singing or swearing when he returned late at night, drunk and boisterous, from the brothels or sing-song houses, accompanied by his slave Ah Wai. Master's bedroom was only four rooms from where I slept, and in the depths of the night I heard him vomit or cough, and sometimes his laughter and the muffled protestings and screamings of women.

The gossip resumed, this time centring on Tai Tai and Master.

'No, she's only twenty-eight, born in the year of the . . .'

'She's been in the House of Tang for at least twelve years.'

'Her youngest daughter is already three.'

'And Master hasn't wanted her for three years!'

'*Aiyah*, men are all alike, it's only when they can't get other women then they'll go with the wife.'

'Hey, Master has been with Ruby and Pearl for the past couple of years now, strange that they're still not pregnant.'

'But it's not every night that he takes Ruby and Pearl, once in a week or so, most of the time he goes to the sing-song house and brothel.'

'Why isn't Jade sent to him?'

'*Aiyah*, don't you know Jade hasn't got her "horsy" yet? Tai Tai doesn't permit because she's not ripe.'

'At seventeen, still no "horsy"?'

'Hard to believe.'

One morning I couldn't help joining in the conversation. 'Why are Pearl and Jade allowed to be with Master, with Tai Tai's knowledge and permission?'

Tang Ma sighed. 'Slaves have no choice. They came with Tai Tai as part of her dowry, and they're special slaves, four blood sisters, they're from a middle-class family, well educated, it was only when their father died and they found themselves in debt that they had to be sold.'

'That explains why they look so much alike. I have difficulty telling them apart sometimes.'

'It's usual for the Master to take the slaves, especially when they're pretty, and even if they don't become concubines, their children are still retained by the family,' Tang Ma went on. 'It's not up to Tai Tai to protest against Master's behaviour, rather it's to her benefit to encourage him to take the slaves, or he'll frequent women outside the House. Rich men can take as many women as they can afford. Huh, it's a tragic life for women.'

'In my next life I'd like to be a male.'

Time passed quickly with all the gossiping, so that every morning I had to rush back to Tai Tai to help her to her marble wash-table when she got up. While Jade fetched hot water from the kitchen, Pearl laid out a porcelain basin, muslin face cloth, soap dish, fresh twig for toothbrush, fine salt as toothpaste, mirrors, and beauty-case, with all Tai Tai's make-up and hair ornaments.

My task was to attend to her feet, while she was having her hair combed by Jade and Pearl. I removed her bedsocks to immerse her feet in a basin of hot water boiled with monkey's bones. The first time I saw Tai Tai's bound feet, I was so horrified that I nearly fainted. Feet so deformed, stunted and crumpled, with only a big toe bent across the stump, the toenail blackened, warped and thick. The other toes were all squashed, flattened and crammed under the arch of the foot. The stench was overwhelming and nauseating. I learned to hold my breath as long as I could while I rubbed her feet with a pure olive oil to soften the callouses at the pressure points, and then wiped them dry before placing them into her satin shoes, three inches long, finely embroidered in colours and designs matching the dress she had chosen for the day.

During this ritual Tai Tai repeatedly lamented her bound feet.

'I will never allow my daughters to have their feet bound. Such a crippling practice. I'm glad the revolutionary leader Mr Sun Yat-sen had stopped women from binding feet, and encouraged men to cut off their queue . . . Huh,' she would sigh, 'look at me with my useless stumps for feet. And the suffering I endured during the binding, and the aches now, the shooting pain when I remain on my feet too long, and the arthritic pains that gnaw me at night . . . Supposed to be dainty and erotic. What nonsense. Once you have borne children with a man he gets bored and goes to womanise elsewhere. You people with natural feet are very lucky, you can move and run. I'm confined to this house, can only totter.'

'None of the women in my village had bound feet,' I told her. 'The first time I saw them was when the refugees passed through Lung Sun.'

I had been cautioned by Tang Ma and Ho Ma never to contradict or argue with our boss, and never to report any gossip I had heard to her. So I always kept my response to a minimum.

When the cook brought Tai Tai her breakfast, she sent the three slave girls to the washroom for their toiletery. Tai Tai breakfasted in the hall in the atrium, often alone. Her favourite dishes were ordered the night before: bird's nest porridge, gingko nut soup with egg-white, and wild ginseng tea. All allegedly helped to maintain her flawless complexion.

After breakfast Tai Tai received her six daughters. All were neatly dressed in coloured silk, their hair groomed in pigtails with coloured ribbons. They came to pay their respect with their *naimas*, before attending classes at the school in the front row of buildings.

I looked at the girls with envy. I wished I were one of the *naimas* so that I could sneak into the classroom and learn something as well. I know most of the *naimas*, who stood behind the girls' desks helping them grind ink from the ink stick, had learnt a few characters, and been enlightened by the tutor's words.

Tang Ma, who had followed Master to class, could recite passages from the classics and had memorised poems by the great Tang and Ming poets and scholars.

The coloured silk dresses the girls wore made me think of our family friend Lee Sao, who had been a silk weaver in Lung Sun. She would collect hundreds of silkworms from the mulberry trees, rear them only to boil them in their cocoons to separate the silky strands, then spend days selecting the good cocoons, and more days in spinning, looming, weaving, dyeing, before taking a length of silk to sell to the cloth merchant.

'Takes about five hundred to one thousand cocoons to make a tunic, depending on the thickness of the material,' she told me once.

It took Lee Sao weeks to complete a yard length; everything was done by hand, and for all that trouble she earned at the most a silver, or a few coppers. And the remains, that is the worms or their casts, she deep-fried after seasoning in salt and pepper, sometimes in a batter, and she would give us some, a delicacy we much appreciated and looked forward to.

I looked at Tai Tai's daughters in their coloured silk, and wondered how many cocoons it had taken to make just one of their pretty dresses.

After the girls went to school it was time for prayers and offerings to Kuan Yin. A porcelain statue of her stood in the atrium and Jade placed fresh flowers, fruits, candies and cakes on the altar table. I lighted the oil-wick lamp and two incense sticks and laid a cushion on the wooden floor for Tai Tai to kneel on in prayer.

Hear our cry
goddess of mercy
and fertility.
Help our family
Multiply.

Last month, ACCA (the Australian Chinese Community Association), took us, a group of frail and elderly Chinese, to visit a nursing home in Earlwood. It's run by a Chinese syndicate for the Chinese in Sydney, and there I saw a ninety year old woman with bound feet, just like those of Tai Tai and the Ancient Mistress, but this woman wore a pair of child-size Reebok shoes and walked with the aid of a walking frame. She had just finished her breakfast — porridge with hundred year old egg — and was going to the activity room to start her game of *mah-jong*. And I thought of the ten years I worked for Tai Tai in the House of Tang, and I wonder if she's still alive. She'd be in her nineties now, and perhaps senile and grumpy, still complaining about the shooting pain from her bound feet, confined to a nursing home, either in Taiwan or the United States. And for many nights after that visit to Earlwood I was filled with guilt for having deserted Tai Tai, for going to Hong Kong instead to join my 'sisters'. Tai Tai often appears in my dreams, dressed in silk edged with fine embroideries and her matching 'three inch lotus', her face powdered white with black fringe on her forehead, a long silk hankie flying lightly from her wrist. A picture of eroticism, delicate as a porcelain doll. And I can still hear Tang Ma recite her poem, 'A lady with lotus feet', during the hair-combing session in the courtyard in the morning.

> Bound feet,
> sensual appeal
> Fairy-like on
> Three inch lotus
> walk and sway
> like willows
> in the wind,
>
> Erotic and sensuous
> fill men with pride
> To possess such wives
> Two stumps quite useless
> for motion purposes
> From the age of five
> bound, for prevention
> From growth, expansion
> restricted in ambulation
> No hope of emancipation
> Forever dependent.

Ho Ma and I used to argue with her on the disadvantages of binding one's feet, but Tang Ma insisted: '*Aiyah*, women's fate depends on their bound feet. Men of status and wealth only choose wives with small feet. People with natural feet like ours are only fit to be servants and slaves; only poor peasants would marry us. Bound feet are women's only qualification for a comfortable and better quality life.'

Tai Tai moved in slow, unsteady shuffles, and could never wander further from her chambers than the perfumed garden or the Garden of Eternal Tranquility. She left the House of Tang only once a year to visit the Temple for prayers on New Year Festival day, carried in a sedan chair, all canopied and covered.

Tai Tai confided in me: '*Aiyah*, I dread my daily visits to the Ancient Mistress.'

It was her duty as a daughter-in-law to pay daily respects to the Ancient Mistress, who resided in the west wing on the row facing the Garden of Eternal Tranquility. On the same row, in the east wing, lived the Old Lord, the senile grandfather of Master.

Jade and Pearl walked on first to announce Tai Tai's visit, while Ruby and I inched along the covered walkway supporting Tai Tai, and enjoying the colour and scent of the flowers in the perfumed garden.

As we entered the reception hall, Tai Tai kowtowed to the Ancient Mistress, a diminutive figure in a loose silk gown of turquoise blue, propped up with satin cushions on a settee finely carved and studded with mother-of-pearl. Tai Tai offered a cup of hot tea with both hands to the Ancient Mistress as the duty of a daughter-in-law.

'And I hope the Ancient One is well today,' Tai Tai said by way of enquiring after her health.

'*Aiyah!* The usual aches and pain in my old bones.' And she indicated where the trouble spots were, her slave Peony standing behind her applying gentle massage with her deft fingers.

Tang Ma had mentioned that the Ancient Mistress came to the House of Tang as a child-bride at the age of ten. She must have been about sixty now, only five years older than Tang Ma, yet she was shrivelled, like a preserved plum, her face wrinkled, eyes lustreless, lines radiating from the corners of her mouth and eyes, and deep furrows in her forehead. But her voice was still loud and piercing.

'Before I die, I wish to have a grandson,' she said. 'The matchmaker sent me this photo, to match Master for a concubine. It's important for the Master, the first-born of the family, to have a son to continue the family line.' She waved her hands about, and her gold and jade bangles clinked and clanked as her voice became shaky with emotion. The speech had tired her; she yawned, was bothered by a general itch, she scratched her skin with her long sharp nails, and called out to Peach, another of her slave girls.

'Help me to the smoking room.'

She was perspiring, her teeth clattering, and saliva started to dribble from her mouth. She shivered and trembled. Peach and I helped her to the smoking room and laid her down on the well-cushioned opium bed, resting her head on a blue and white porcelain pillow, and supporting her arm on an arm-rest. Peony was roasting pellets of opium on a stick like a knitting needle over an oil lamp, before feeding them into the pipe.

Opium — the 'black mud' — the very stuff that had been condemned by the village storyteller as an evil, a dissipation, a bad habit, the cause of ruin and poverty; a vice which the Ancient Mistress indulged in style, from a pipe made of jade and ivory. I had heard that opium could only be bought in the black-market, but in my village, where most peasants lived from hand to mouth, no one could afford to have even one puff. I remembered the tale of a mischievous monk who smoked opium for the first time, and soon after he felt as if he was going mad; he turned somersault, walked upside down on his hands, and imagined himself to be a demigod. The room, walls and ceiling, began to expand, and he felt inspired to compose poetry and paint; but the words were illegible and the painting was like the wretched scratch of a fly.

Tai Tai sat on the edge of the opium bed, staring at the photograph of a young girl left by the matchmaker while the Ancient Mistress sucked hungrily on the ivory mouthpiece of the pipe, inhaling every vapour. Quickly her tension eased, she closed her eyes and declared she was seeing girls fecund with male babies. Peony mopped her brow with a cloth scented with rose-water. The pungent smell of opium pervaded the room, wafting into the corridor outside.

'They're selling it as a perfume in a bottle now, by the French couturier Yves St Laurent.' Kim returns from an overseas trip with a gift. 'Hope it'll bring you many pleasant memories,' she says.

'The black mud sold in a bottle?'

'*Aiyah*, it's not cheap *yiah*. Sixty dollars duty free for the dark liquid.'

I press the top and a puff of pungent mist is released. 'It's not the same.' I shake my head. 'Not at all like the opium odour that wafted in the corridor outside the smoking room of the Ancient Mistress. You've been cheated.'

'What's the genuine stuff smell like then?'

'Strong, sweet and spicy. Exotic. Very hard to describe. The olfactory sense is something individual which you alone sample and recognise. And you either like or hate it.'

When I was in Singapore, I had my first smell of durian, the king of tropical fruit. I liked it immediately, a powerful odour most people label as stinking, like 'bad cheese' or the 'turds of cats.'

Tai Tai said: 'May I be so bold as to tell the Ancient Mistress that our House of Tang is going to have a baby boy before the end of the year?'

'Uh, are you pregnant again?'

'No, but Gold my slave girl is, with Master's seed, and according to the soothsayer it is going to be a boy.'

'Bring her to me at once,' the Ancient Mistress demanded.

'Gold is resting in the Vegetarian Hall of the nunnery.'

'Why send her to the Vegetarian Hall, isn't our house good enough for her?'

'*Aiyah*, she gets rest and good attention there, the nuns have some medical knowledge, and as we are the benefactors of the nunnery, she gets special treatment. At home she might risk a miscarriage with Master often drunk and wanting to bed her. Tang Ma and the cook visit her every day, taking her special brewed herbs and chicken broth.'

But the Ancient Mistress was no longer listening. She snored, oblivious to the world.

One morning during the hair-combing session Tang Ma asked me: 'Why was Tai Tai so upset yesterday?'

'I heard a terrible commotion coming from her room when I was walking through the Garden of Eternal Tranquility,' Ho Ma added. 'She sounded as if in a great rage, shouting and yelling and the slaves were crying and screaming.'

'It happened after the visit of Ah Wai, the man-servant of Master,' I replied. 'He brought some papers to show her.'

'I bet you Master has been losing at gambling again, the IOU chits,' Ho Ma said. 'But it's unfair to treat the three slave girls as scapegoats.'

I was familiar with such rowdy scenarios, my sisters and I had been scapegoats to my Papa and elder brothers, when they came home tired from their work in the field, shouting and yelling at us, hitting us with brutal force. We would cry and scream, cowering in a corner.

Master's gambling debts upset and depressed Tai Tai, and she took it out on the slaves. At the slightest excuse she caned them, pulled their hair and ears, or burned their fingers with the lighted ends of joss sticks. Crying and bawling, the slaves begged for mercy by pulling their ears — a sign of repentance. And they knelt to offer Tai Tai cups of tea, to appease her anger. I was exempted from such punishment, I never became a target for her temper, but I too knelt down to beg her to spare the slave girls.

Tang Ma said: 'Lucky you're a "comb-up", she won't beat you unless you've done something wrong. Besides, you have the freedom to resign and walk out if she ill-treats you.'

That night I was wakened up by some strange rustling sounds. My first impulse was to rush in to see if Tai Tai needed a chamberpot, but Pearl and Ruby, who slept in the same antechamber as me, restrained me.

'Sh-sh.' Pearl signalled me not to speak.

And through the curtain of hanging beads at the threshold to Tai Tai's room I saw the distinct silhouette of Master, stout and paunchy, standing at Tai Tai's bed. There was a full moon bathing the room in light. Through the mosquito net Master was pulling and tugging, and Tai Tai was struggling. Amid her groans and growls, the bed shook, as Master mounted her and started moving, like riding a horse.

Faster and faster, Master moved, heaving and breathing laboriously, forcing his way in between Tai Tai's thighs. And the moon shone through the shutters of the window over the pair of them, Master frantic and urgent, Tai Tai passive but noisy, her 'three inch lotus' straddling Master's shoulders. She uttered a shrill cry as if in great suffering or pain: 'Stop, stop, I can't stand it, I'm dying, I'm dying . . .' Then Master, exhausted, collapsed on top of her, and all the squeaking of the bed stopped, and in the quiet I saw the shadows of their intertwining limbs, bare as their clothes were pulled up, dishevelled, in the silvery light of the moon.

Master spoke, in a teasing tone: 'You enjoyed that, didn't you, admit it.'

'*Aiyah*, you're an animal.' Tai Tai's voice was soft and soothing. Soon I heard Master snoring, and they were lying side by side. The moon continued to make lines of shadows through the shutters of the windows, and I heard a cat meow in the distance, followed by the hoot of an owl.

We crept back to our beds. Pearl whispered: 'It's time she got a taste of his medicine.'

And I lay there, shocked and still. I felt sorry for Tai Tai and Pearl and Ruby who suffered such violent attacks, such acts of aggression, and I cried when I thought of my blood sisters who were sold as slaves or to the brothel. I was glad that my new sisters and I had taken the vow of marriage-resistance, and all of a sudden I missed them all for we had only known each other two days.

I remember seeing a dog in my village mounting another, both dogs panting and whining, their tongues dripping saliva. My mother shouted at me to get indoors, forbiding me to watch any more.

'No shame, you mustn't watch such obscene acts, you're still a virgin,' she scolded. 'Unmarried girls should be chaste and virtuous, their virginity preserved intact, and watching such animal behaviour is bad.'

I didn't understand then, but now I realised what she had meant by her constant warning: 'Be careful, now that you 'ride the horsy' you could get pregnant by men'. And I concluded that that was how Gold had become pregnant. But I was still puzzled about Jade not being 'ripe' because she hadn't ridden the 'horsy' and why she wasn't allowed to serve the Master.

The following morning I saw Master breakfasting with Tai Tai for the first time since I had come to the House of Tang.

'Only when he needs Tai Tai to validate the IOU notes for the accountant to pay his debts, does he come to butter her up. She holds the purse strings,' Tang Ma said.

Ho Ma shook her head sadly. 'He'll ruin the family's fortune, gambling and womanising at this rate. I was his *naima* right from the day he was born, he was such a sweet baby too. But thoroughly spoilt by his mother when his father died, all his whims and fancies indulged.'

'Fortunately Tai Tai has a good business sense and can mind the family business.'

'What is the family business?' I asked.

'*Aiyah*, don't you know? The House of Tang is the largest merchant in dried seafood, we're the only exporter who own freighters for shipping the goods to south-east Asia.'

Three months after I arrived at the House of Tang came the August Moon Festival — the fifteenth day of the eighth moon — when the moon is at its brightest and roundest in the whole year. The moon is a goddess, and this is the time for worshipping her with cakes fashioned in her image — cakes made of flat round pastry, with stuffing of sweet bean or lotus paste, or sometimes salted egg-yolks.

In Lung Sun, mooncakes were for sale a month before the Festival. But Papa waited until the day after the Festival to buy them for half the price. So we always had mooncakes to eat only after the celebrations were over. But in the House of Tang, the Moon Festival was celebrated in a big way.

In the first courtyard, the cobbled stone one, a platform was erected with bamboo poles for viewing the parade of lanterns and floats.

The children — Tai Tai's six daughters, those of the servants, and the illegitimate ones of the four Masters — played with paper lanterns. Paper rabbits on wheels, lanterns shaped as lotus, butterflies, ducks. I loved the horses — split in two, one half was carried in front, the other strapped upon the children's backs so that they looked as though they were walking horses. All were lit by candles.

Master, Tai Tai, the Ancient Mistress, and all the servants and maids were on the stage to watch the parade. On a long table a large urn of burning incense and candles on sticks were displayed among plates of cooked yams, snails, mooncakes, pomelos, and tangerines. These were offered first to the the Moon Goddess and later to us humans.

The street outside was packed with pedestrians: lovers walking hand-in-hand; families and friends sauntering, talking; itinerant hawkers selling fruits, drinks, mooncakes . . .

In the middle of the celebrations, a messenger from the nunnery came looking for Tang Ma. Gold was in labour. Before he could catch his breath, another messenger followed.

'It's a baby boy, a male!'

'*Aiyah*, a male, Tai Tai. Ancient Mistress, Master, Gold has given birth to a boy!' Tang Ma shouted, and the whole clan clapped their hands in applause.

'The first son of Master, a grandson to the Ancient Mistress, the great-grandson to the Old Lord, a lineage for the House of Tang.'

The good news was announced and spread quickly throughout the streets of Canton, for the House of Tang was well-known, held in high esteem by all the merchants and 'Hongs' of Canton. Strings of firecrackers exploded as the huge black lacquered doors were opened and free mooncakes were distributed to the poor and the beggars. Crowds formed outside, below the steps guarded by the stone lions. The messengers were rewarded with red-packets of good luck money.

The same night Tai Tai dispatched Tang Ma and Wu Ma by sedan chairs to the nunnery.

'Bring the baby back early tomorrow morning, Tang Ma, wrap him warm in the new baby blanket.'

And to Wu Ma, Tai Tai instructed: 'Stay and look after Gold during the post-natal month. See that she has plenty of rest. Cook her the usual ginger, chicken and herbal *tong kwei* tonic broth, and black vinegar and pigs' trotters. Here's your red-packet of good luck money, and when you complete the month you'll be generously awarded with a bonus.'

'What is companion of the month?' I asked Ho Ma.

Ho Ma explained to me, an ignorant peasant: 'The month after giving birth the woman is considered to be dirty, full of the evils from the discharge of her womb. She has to be quarantined from the rest of the family, especially the men, her clothes and underwear are washed and hung separately, she's confined to her room, not allowed to bathe or be exposed to the air, in case bad winds enter her and cause complications.'

'But my mother had sixteen pregnancies and had no companion at all.'

'*Aiyah*, life is cheap with the poor peasants, how can they afford a companion of the month who commands a very high fee?'

A new *naima* started work in the House of Tang, the morning after the birth of Gold's baby. Tai Tai had interviewed her a month before. She was chosen out of a handful who had come that day.

Tai Tai began the interview by asking: 'What is your name and age?'

'Your humble servant's surname is Chu and I'm sixteeen years old,' she said.

'And your experience in breast-feeding?'

'I've a three-month-old baby at home who is breast fed.'

'And with a young baby how can you manage this job?'

'I need to supplement my family's income,' she sobbed, tears rolling down her cheeks. 'My husband is a rickshaw-puller, and his meagre income is not enough to support his parents, who are opium addicts, plus ten younger brothers and sisters.'

'And what about your son?'

'My mother-in-law and her children will look after him. It's time to wean him to a soft diet.'

'Well, your salary will be ten pieces of silver per month, doubled at the New Year, with a generous bonus. The conditions are: the lactation must be maintained till such time as the baby is weaned to solid food.'

'No problem, my milk is copious . . .'

'You're allowed home once a year, but once a month and on special circumstances, day visitors are permitted. You will sleep in the baby's room, and care for him and feed him day and night. Once a day you will bring baby to visit me, as well as to his grandmother, the Ancient Mistress, and his great-grandfather, the Old Lord.'

'Yes, Tai Tai.'

'Also, when you're visiting the great-grandfather you will breast-feed the Old Lord too.'

'Breast-feed the Old Lord! Do I hear right?'

'Yes, the Old Lord. He needs to be breast-fed once a day.'

'No, I can't. I have a husband. He . . .'

'He just wants to be rejuvenated. Humour him, and he'll double your salary.'

'Twenty pieces of silver per month! I'll earn more in one month than my husband in half a year!'

Tai Tai reaffirmed: 'You will not regret coming to work here; forget about your husband and your child. The House of Tang is your family now. My son will be your charge, you are his *naima*. He'll cling to your bosom more than to mine.'

'But breast-feeding a grown man! How embarrassing!'

'The Old Lord is harmless, a senile, toothless old man in

his mid-eighties. His second childhood. Just play along with him.'

The Chinese believe that breast-feeding an old person helps him to recapture his manhood and retain longevity. When I think of Chu Naima, a particular story from the twenty-four classical stories of the 'filial obedience or piety,' comes to mind. A daughter-in-law breast-fed her elderly mother-in-law in the time of famine, giving her priority before feeding her young baby. There was no milk left for the baby, and he starved to death. Such filial piety is supposed to be rewarded richly in the next life, or command high respect from the community of the time. It is a very important duty of the son or daughter, according to the teaching of Mencius.

Chu Naima was the privileged wet-nurse in the House of Tang, as she catered for two special people: the youngest of the household, and the oldest. She was fed the choice cuts of chicken, pork, lamb, fish; and a special chef steamed her broth of chicken or extract of meat, brewed in claypots with a concoction of nuts and herbs, according to a secret formula for enriching the protein in milk. She was the envy of all the other servants, as she had free choice of fresh fruits and vegetables and whatever exotic nutritious food she desired.

I obtained a time-honoured recipe from the cook, well proven for sustaining lactation.

Duck stew with Cordeseps Sinensis:
Place the duck, without its viscera, in an earthenware pot.
Add five to ten pieces of Cordeseps Sinensis with three slices of ginger, a scallion, a rice-bowl of water. Stew over a slow heat until well cooked. (Cordeseps Sinensis is also

known as Chinese caterpillar fungus, it contains crude proteins, coarse fibres, and carbohydrates.)

When the baby was one month old a banquet was held in celebration of his full-month; an important milestone. He was named Ming Ming, 'brilliant and bright', a name chosen by the soothsayer, according to the 'eight characters' of his horoscope — hour, date, month and year, (each time component has two characters) — and the five elements of fire, water, earth, wood and gold. On that day, he was dressed in a red gown, and wore shoes embroidered with the face of a tiger. His head was shaved by Tai Tai in a special ceremony, before he was carried to the Temple by Master himself in a sedan-chair to pray to the ancestors' tablets of the House of Tang.

That night, a banquet was held for friends and relatives. Chu Naima carried the baby, following Tai Tai who hobbled with my support from table to table, thanking the guests for their gifts of red-packets of good luck money and their attendance at the banquet. Each guest was given a pair of hard-boiled eggs tinged with red, and slices of pickled ginger — symbols of fertility and lineage.

But Gold, the biological mother, was not included in this celebration. Wu Ma, her 'companion of the month', had finished her job, and left her confined in the nunnery. According to Wu Ma's gossip, Gold had attempted suicide by swallowing her hairpin but was stopped in time. After her recovery she shaved her hair and became a nun.

'*Aiyah*, she realised that she was made use of — a vehicle for breeding the baby, without any reward from either Tai Tai or Master,' Ho Ma said.

I sympathised with Gold. I thought I would have done the same, in her place. I knew of a few ways to take one's own life — again from the tales told by the village story-teller: drinking poison, drowning in a well (Pearl concubine was drowned by a eunuch after she incurred the wrath of Empress Dowager), hanging oneself from the rafter of the ceiling, swallowing a sharp object like a hairpin, or slicing one's wrist.

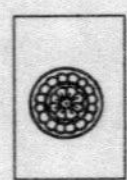

'So you see I have a few tricks up my sleeve in case I should meet with adverse conditions,' I brag to Kim.

'These methods are all out of date. Sleeping pills are the best, you lie in your own bed, dream of your adventurous past, and exit,' Kim advocates.

'I heard on the radio that there's a doctor in America who kills his patients at their request.'

'Oh that's different, it's called euthanasia. It's meant for those suffering from terminal illnesses without hope of recovery, it doesn't cater for personal problems of the kind Gold experienced. It's very controversial, it's a crime to do that here.'

I must be eighty-three or so by now, but each year I still look forward with excitement to the Chinese New Year or Spring Festival — as it's commonly known in China. It's the start of fifteen days of celebration. Here in Sydney, the main attraction is the lion dance accompanied by drums, gongs and cymbals, amidst explosions of red firecrackers. These displays attract large crowds of onlookers, requiring police control.

When I arrived twenty years ago, Chinatown was confined to Dixon and Campbell Streets, with perhaps half a dozen Chinese restaurants and two or three dim and cluttered Chinese groceries, standing next to large old warehouses. Behind Dixon Street was the wholesale vegetable market, a bustle of commotion in the mornings and when the sales or auctions were over, the lane and gutters strewn with odds and ends of half rotten vegetables which would have fed all the beggars in the Ancestral Temple of Fok Sun. Dixon Street was badly lit and spooky then, and I could hear the clacking of *mah-jong* tiles at the corner of Dixon Street and the service station, which has long since been demolished. A new concrete block with escalator stands in its stead. At a small home-style cooking restaurant called Sun Ah, that first New Year in Australia, we ordered the humble noodle and won-ton soup. Kim couldn't find it in the menu. The waiter said 'You mean the "long and short" soup?' We giggled at the ridiculous but descriptive name.

Now Chinatown has spread from Dixon to Sussex, Thomas, Hay and George Streets, and I can't keep up with the number of restaurants, supermarkets and the myriad of cafes and smaller takeaway shops with cooked food, roast duck and barbeque pork, braised intestines of pigs.

On the seventh day of the New Year, which is 'everybody's birthday', Kim, Suchin and myself and our Chinese friends celebrate at a local restaurant, seated at a round table to sample the special New Year dishes with names suggestive of good omen. A dish of pigs' trotters stewed with black hairy fungus is translated as 'May unexpected windfall come into your hand.' I've backed the winning horse in the Melbourne Cup race three years in a row now, ever since I ordered the pigs' trotters; I highly recommend it for the gamblers. I'm a timid gambler myself, I bet only two dollars each way, once a year in November, but this year my winnings total forty-two dollars. I don't know one horse from another, and only choose one with number six, *loc* in Cantonese, which puns with good living. At New Year all the shop fronts are plastered with red-paper covered with black Chinese characters of good luck and good fortune, like the couplets Papa used to paste on our creaky doors, and from the shop awnings dangle green lettuce tied with a red-packet for the dancing lions to retrieve.

'A disguise of protection money,' my neighbour, Mrs Chin, tells me. 'And the money in the red-packet must be at least five hundred dollars,' she continues. Mrs Chin has a friend who is a part-owner of a shop in Chinatown. I am not surprised by what she says. For three years in Hong Kong I handed over protection money to a person known only by number, not by name, on behalf of my boss, the actress-singer Little Peacock Lien, so I am familiar with the protection money racket. It is a way of life with the Chinese, a 'donation' from those well-to-do to an anonymous syndicate. I hope they divide the money up and give to those not doing so well. If you refuse to pay, your business or livelihood will be threatened. I've heard that the Triads have infiltrated Australia, and I wonder which group my brother Ah Sai belonged to, as I never dared ask him, and only saw his insignia, a triangle, tattooed on his arm. Recently a member of the Seventeen K has been arrested for smuggling 'white powder' (heroin) inside the hollow plastic tiles of *mah-jong* sets. Opium, the 'black mud' is now obsolete. Kim tells me people sniff the white powder or inject it through their veins now. And it's the younger generation that becomes addicted.

'What's the significance of the Chinese New Year and all these animals each year is supposed to represent?' Kim asks. 'Christmas celebrates the birth of Christ, and is documented in the Bible; although nowadays it's become very commercialised.'

I cannot really answer her question satisfactorily; all my knowledge is acquired from stories told by the village storyteller, the gossip session at the House of Tang, and later from Au Ma in Hong Kong. Women in my time were not educated except for a very privileged few. We gossiped a great deal, and the information was passed down by word of mouth. Women talked, told stories, true or imaginary, as most were confined within the house and its neighbourhood. Wagging of the tongue caused many troubles in those days among the in-laws all living together as an extended family, as it still does today. Though each family lives apart, they can conveniently gossip on the phone. In old China, talkativeness was one of the grounds for a husband to file for a divorce, the other two being adultery and barrenness.

'But why all the fuss of celebrating, all the lion and dragon dances and firecrackers, is it just an excuse to eat and visit friends, or is there a religious origin?'

'It's a rebirth, a new start, a renovating or rejuvenating of the deities,' I try to explain.

'What gods?'

'The Kitchen God returns from reporting to the heavens, full of energy to start the New Year and protect the household afresh.'

'I'd like to know about the various animals of the year,' Kim goes on. 'My Australian colleagues are interested to know which their birth year animal is; they read their horoscopes in magazines and ask me for more information.'

'There are twelve years in the cycle and each is a lunar year; each month starts with the waxing and waning of the moon, which reaches its fullest at the middle of the month, the fifteenth. Sometimes there's an extra month in a year. Each year is represented by an animal, all are domestic, except for the tiger and the dragon. There's a rhyme I learned off by heart in the House of Tang from the seamstress who used to sew my suit; she would recite in a sing-song way to herself at work, and I would sit there waiting for my suit and repeating by rote after her:

The leader is the RAT
followed by the OX
next is TIGER, the big cat
and bunny RABBIT in its hop.

The mythical DRAGON
majestic with claws and fire,
trailing in its wake,
its little dragon
the wriggling SNAKE;
then comes
the gallop of the HORSE
alarming the grazing GOAT
to a pause.
MONKEY is the most mischevious
ruffling the ROOSTER's feathers
the DOG jumps and barks
while the sleeping PIG snores,
and the RAT comes round once more.

'That's how I work out which animal comes next.'

'That's a great help, my colleagues will have to count in cycles of twelve for their birth sign.' Kim writes down the order of the animals and the years they correspond to — monkey: 1992, goat: 1991 . . .

Tang Ma's recitation comes to my mind: 'Men at first are radically good'. It is the first sentence from the 'three word classics,' which the masters and misses learned off by heart, sometimes without knowing its meaning or implication.

'The Chinese regard their New Year in the same light. The start of a year is like a rebirth, and should be radically good, the end of the existing year is phasing out with all its bad luck and unfortunate happenings, and all preparations are made to welcome the new year. Every door is an entry to riches, every house is decorated like a palace, and every man acts and dresses like a VIP in his new suit and shoes with many red-packets to give away to children, and the unmarrieds,' I explain to Kim.

During my years in the village, New Year was the only time Papa took stock of his children, lining them in a row to count the number of mouths he had to feed and the yardage of cloth he had to buy. We started sewing our new suits and shoes a month beforehand. But in the House of Tang, my measurements were taken by the seamstress, and a cloth merchant was called in with his samples for Tang Ma and Ho Ma to decide on the quality, colour and texture. For me as a 'comb-up', white for my tunic and black for pants, cotton for summer and spring, thicker calico and quilted material for winter.

Tai Tai herself selected the cloth for her daughters and the slaves. She would quote a wise saying: 'The schedule for the whole year is planned in Spring.' Tai Tai took a whole day to pick her own wardrobe. A special tailor from Shanghai came in with illustrations of the latest designs and bales of silk, pelts of fur and pieces of leather, and light quilted satin for the milder seasons. And her shoes, the 'three inch lotus', were designed to match her dresses. The five seamstresses in the House of Tang would get busy embroidering, knitting, crocheting and quilting, or sewing with furs and leather.

A month before the end of the year, the House of Tang bustled with preparations for the New Year. Carpenters, handymen and painters were summoned to do the spring cleaning, white-washing, and general repairs of the houses.

The goldsmiths came next, with suggestion for the latest designs. They urged Tai Tai to stock up on gold.

'The Japanese are invading China in the north, lots of refugees are fleeing, gold is the only easy portable asset they can carry.'

'Mrs Sung, my *mah-jong* friend, tells me we're winning the war . . .' Tai Tai said.

'*Aiyah*, hard to say, we Chinese are split into two parties, one led by Chiang Kai-shek, and the other by Chou En-lai, and at one stage they were united to fight against the Japanese, but the latest I've heard is Chiang is purging and killing the Communists.'

'Mr Sung is in charge of an army of Chiang's Kuomintang group.'

'If we Chinese cannot unite, the foreigners will take advantage of the situation, sooner or later the wars will spread south.'

'I better invest in gold jewellery,' Tai Tai decided. 'Make me some pure gold necklaces and bangles as thick and solid as you can, for me and my daughters.'

The cooks were busy making glutinous rice-flour, an essential ingredient of the special New Year sesame seed fritters and the traditional steamed cake.

Two weeks before the New Year, prayers and offerings were made to send the Kitchen God off to heaven. Before his image was burnt, his lips were smeared with honey and wine so that, drunk and bribed, he would have sweet reports for the gods in heaven. And our household would continue to be blessed for the coming New Year.

The men servants placed large Ming and Ching vases in the official reception hall, and all the halls of the buildings. I helped to cut and trim stalks of plum and cherry blossoms, and Tang Ma and Ho Ma arranged them in vases. Pots of cumquat heavy with fruit were placed indoors as decoration. The slaves filled plates with sweetmeats and dried red melon seeds for visitors to munch.

On New Year's Eve, all members of the House of Tang sat at the round table in the official reception hall for the family gathering dinner of vegetarian dishes. At the hour of the rat — eleven o'clock — firecrackers exploded to welcome in the New Year, sending off the old with all its bad luck.

On the morning of the New Year, I hurried to the toilet, washed myself, and dressed in a new suit of white starched tunic and baggy black silk pants. My hair had grown down to my ears, and I tied it into two small bunches, each secured with a red string. I wore a new pair of thick calico black shoes, and rushed here and there with my hands clasped wishing all the fellow servants a happy and prosperous New Year. As to Tai Tai, Master, Ancient Mistress and the Old Lord, I knelt with a hot cup of tea with red dates and offered them all the blessings of the season. In return they gave me red-packets of good luck money. It was a day of rest for the servants as no one was allowed to sweep the floor — in case good luck is swept away — or use sharp instruments like scissors or knives — symbolic of fighting or quarrelling. On this day, once a year, we servants were allowed some leisure time. I joined in a *mah-jong* game with Tang Ma, Ho Ma and Wu Ma. Most of the men played cards. The slaves and I were never close, they kept to themselves, knowing I was not the same as them. I was a 'comb-up', and also a wage-earner, of different status.

So there existed a barrier between us, of envy and resentment. The slaves were not allowed out of the House of Tang, not even on New Year. But all I could think about was the second day of New Year, when I could meet Uncle Fatty Lee and Ah Sai and my three sisters.

The next morning I was up even earlier than usual and, dressed in my new suit and new shoes, with money in the hidden pockets of my belt and tunic, I dashed down the winding path, retracing the route I had taken when I first entered the House of Tang. The gatekeeper came out to stare at me. He too was dressed in new clothes, and his hair was cut and groomed. I wished him seasonal greetings, and his wife peeped out of the door, with a new babe in arms.

Then I heard the familiar voice of Ah Sai, and the cackle of Uncle Fatty Lee, and saw them approaching, followed closely by Han, Yin and Fong, all dressed in white tunics and black pants, our trademark.

'*Aiyah*, Uncle Fatty Lee and Ah Sai and sisters — happy New Year!'

It was one of the happiest moments of my life.

Ah Han's face was still long, like a horse, but she had grown fatter. Ah Yin wasn't much different, her dimples deep in her apple face. Ah Fong, the bamboo pole, had shot up an inch, and expanded sideways too.

'Ah Sai, have you been good? Have you learned any handiwork?'

He had grown another three or four inches taller, and

was too shy even to hold my hand, but looked well-fed. He wore a clean shirt that was much too large for him.

'Who gave you such a big shirt?'

'It's a hand-me-down from the boss,' Uncle Fatty Lee replied on Ah Sai's behalf. And Uncle Fatty Lee said: 'Today we'll walk the streets of Canton, there's so much to see, and we'll eat at the best of the poor men's restaurants tonight before I send you all home.'

Xi Guan was the district of the House of Tang, where houses were hidden behind tall hedges and high walls fortified with jagged pieces of glass. The streets were congested with families of old and young. The rich were carried in sedan-chairs or rickshaws. Children played on the pavement lighting sparklers or firecrackers. Beggars held out their tin cans to beg for alms.

'The sight of the beggars reminds me of the Ancestral Temple,' Ah Han remarked. 'I don't see too many of them in the bazaar.'

'They're chased away during trading time, only invade the place after the stalls are closed,' Uncle Fatty Lee said.

'*Aiyah*, are you allowed out to the bazaar?' I asked in amazement.

'Almost daily, only to trail behind the chef and help carry the shopping.'

'I'm only allowed out one day, that is today,' I said.

'So am I,' Ah Yin said. 'My sewing keeps me busy, embroidering, knitting, darning, patching, altering, for all members of the family. But when Sister Fong goes to the garden to dry her clothes, we are able to see each other and talk over the fence. In my house the male servants go shopping.'

Ah Fong was more fortunate, she sometimes also followed her chief housekeeper to the bazaar, when someone was needed to carry the extra load. 'Our servant knows your Tang Ma and Ho Ma well, they stop and gossip whenever they meet,' she told me.

'Oh good, then you can pass any message for me through them. Tang Ma and Ho Ma are rather friendly with me.'

Ah Han said: 'In that case we can communicate with each other, too. My chef also stops to gossip with your Tang servants. Through your Tang Ma and Ho Ma we learn a lot about what has happened in your place of work: a baby boy was born, a new *naima*, and how you've become the favourite of your Tai Tai.'

Yin and Fong nodded. 'Our Mistresses play *mah-jong* with your Tai Tai almost every day.'

'Madam Sung?'

'Yes, her husband is a general commander of an army in the Kuomintang under Chiang Kia-shek.'

'My boss is commander of the navy, Li Sheki,' Ah Fong said.

'And mine is a Mandarin, a civil servant of the government, in charge of Custom and Excise, the Wu,' said Ah Yin.

As we talked, we walked hand-in-hand, me and Ah Yin (I could feel the callouses in her fingers, from her sewing), Uncle Fatty Lee and Ah Sai, Ah Fong and Ah Han, like one big close happy family.

We left the so-called city wall of Canton and crossed the river. I had a good view of the water as it curled round from Shamien Island. We passed through endless rows of two-storey terraced houses all with their new couplets on red-paper and prints of Door Gods on the door panels. All shops were closed for business.

'For the next fifteen days the celebrations will continue,

feasting, visiting, relaxing, gambling. Most people who work hard only take this period off,' Uncle Fatty Lee said.

Some forty-four years later I find myself viewing, from the air before the aeroplane descends, another river, in another country; a span of crescent-shaped bridge over a harbour, clean and sparkling in brilliant sunshine, with sails of many colours and dashing hydrofoils, and on the northern foreshore there is a park, whose gate is an open mouth with a set of gigantic teeth; and later also on a Chinese New Year's day, Kim and I take Suchin there, this Luna Park for fun, and ride on the swinging pirate ship, screaming our throats hoarse, and see our distorted selves in various shapes — fat, tiny, tall — as we walk through the hall of mirrors, and we throw tennis balls at the open mouths of wooden clowns whose heads move this way and that. And I feel transported back to my teenage days, those second days of the Chinese New Year in Canton, when once a year, my sisters, Uncle Fatty Lee, Ah Sai and I roamed through halls with mirrors that too made us look short, fat, tall and thin, and laughed at our ridiculous shapes and made faces at our images. I remember the open-air markets where itinerant show people set up their stalls. For a few coppers we were admitted to a magic show, watched jugglers, and peeped at the freak shows — the Siamese twins, joined at the buttocks, and a fat lady with webbed feet. I loved the performances of monkeys and trained dogs, and the puppet shows. There was an opera, too, performed on a makeshift stage of bamboo poles by a troupe of professional actors.

'We'll go to the poor man's restaurants,' said Uncle Fatty Lee.

This was two blocks from Uncle Fatty Lee's quarters, an open market alive with roadside stalls. The air smelt of fried garlic and tangy ginger, and the fragrance of five-spiced barbecued meat mingled with that of fresh seafood.

Eating stalls clogged up the whole street. Each competed with the next in the shouting of menus, the ordering of dishes, the announcement of specialities: 'Stewed four-legged reptile with herbs, good for purifying your lungs, your kidney, your liver . . .' Kerosene lamps hung on poles above our heads. Every stall had at least two stoves and woks ablaze. Cauldrons with soup bubbling, boiling, and steaming. We squeezed our way through the crowd to a stall on the other side of the road.

'What's the catch of the day?' Uncle Fatty Lee asked as we sat down on the low bamboo stools at a bamboo table.

The cook, naked to the waist, wiped the sweat off his brow with the towel thrown across one shoulder. He scooped a fish from a wooden tub, and we admired it, thrashing and jumping in his net.

'The freshest groupa alive. Just brought in from the Pearl River,' he said.

Uncle Fatty Lee nodded approvingly.

'I haven't eaten fresh fish for a long time,' said Ah Sai. He was so happy that he clapped his hands and jumped from his stool, laughing and shouting 'Good, good!'

The fish was placed on the chopping block. 'Chop' off came the tail. The cook held the fish in his palm and ran the cleaver against its scales, first one side then the other. He yanked open the gills, and dug out the innards with his bare fingers. Oil was smoking in the wok. The cook tossed in the fish which sizzled, was flipped over, and braised with a mixture of soya sauce, salt, sugar, wine and arrowroot powder. It was served on a dish garnished with a sprig of parsley and a twirl of spring onion, a few shreds of red chilli and showered with ground pepper. Our mouths watered when the dish was set down on our table.

'Eat while it's hot,' Uncle Fatty Lee exhorted us, with chopsticks in hand and rice bowl raised to his lips.

I'm watching a documentary made by some foreign journalist in China. It shows a cook wearing a white cap and a white apron, standing over a red-hot wok on a brazier with leaping flame, and he's sizzling a live fish which he has just scaled. All over the world people are objecting to such cruelty to animals, frying a live fish.

'Before Australians kill their animals in the abbatoir they're injected with an anaesthetic first, put them to sleep, no pain,' Kim tells me.

'What about the lobster shashimi we eat at the Chinese restaurant in Sussex Street, where lobsters are shelled alive, their flesh cut into slices while their eyes are still blinking.'

'That's reflex action,' Kim argues.

'But it's still alive and eyeballs moving. Isn't that cruelty too?'

I must admit we Chinese are a cruel race; we prefer live animals to slaughter for fresh meat, we would never, if given a choice, purchase frozen or thawed meat. The lobster sashimi reminds me of a gruesome torture described by the village storyteller, of how the empress Dowager condemned her enemy to a capital punishment known as *ling chih*. The executioner had to exercise skill in applying one thousand cuts to the victim, so that life was not extinct until the last stab, the thousandth one, right into his heart.

But even so, when the Tiananmen Square massacre was telecast I was stunned at my own people, a cruel race, who killed the young unarmed students in cold blood. We used to refer to the Westerners as 'barbarians', the *feng kwei*, as though we ourselves were the gentle people, the civilised ones with a long history of culture. And I'm ashamed of my country, for I've lived here for twenty years, and I know the Australians, no matter how biased and resentful, would never crush their tanks over anybody unarmed and defenceless.

'It's an issue of human rights,' Kim says.

'It's barbaric, heartless and uncivilised.'

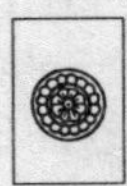

A blind man played his *erh-hu* while a young girl sang in a scratchy voice, and later distributed wrapped liquorice olives to each table. Uncle Fatty Lee gave her a copper.

My sisters and I took our savings of silver money and placed them in red-packets before offering them to Uncle Fatty Lee.

'Please accept, Uncle Fatty Lee, from all of us.'

He nodded and took the red-packets. An older person didn't thank a younger person, especially someone considered close like a relative. In the old Chinese custom, the younger ones were told to respect the elders, to be obedient without questioning, and to do them favours without expecting any gratitude in return.

When I first came to Australia I was impressed by the generous utterances of 'thank you' for little tokens: paying a bus fare, buying a bottle of milk, a loaf of bread.

In old China, only the beggers, the inferiors, the servants, the subjects of the Emperors said 'thank you.'

The wonderful day came too quickly to an end. After Uncle Fatty Lee sent the three sisters home to Xiao Bai, the Little North, Ah Sai and I walked clasping hands. When we reached Xi Guan, at the side gate, I was reluctant to re-enter the House of Tang. How could I bear to wait another twelve months, a whole year, before I saw my folks again? So I cried and asked Uncle Fatty Lee if he could find me a job in Xiao Bai.

'Stay here in the House of Tang, because they treat you well and Tai Tai is fond of you,' he advised. 'There's a lot of unrest in the government and the military, so with the other three families things may not be so stable as in the House of Tang. It's not important seeing us or not, as long as we can send messages to you; look after yourself, work hard, save your money for a "raining day". And don't think of changing your job.'

So I went back to the House of Tang, and in a way, I found comfort in the familiar: the people, the rooms, the courtyards, even in the smell of the various flowers in the perfumed garden, and the opium wafting from the Ancient Mistress' corridor. The touch of the rough and firm callouses of Tai Tai's deformed feet when I massaged them with olive oil, the voice of Tai Tai when she was not in a temper, soft and soothing like spring water, the meow of the cat in the distance in the quiet of the night, and the sudden hoot of the owl.

The usual routine prevailed at the House of Tang, save for one exception: the distraction provided by Chu Naima and Ming Ming. Every day she would push Ming Ming, chubby and fat, in a fine bamboo baby carriage with a canopy, on her usual visits to Tai Tai in the morning and in the late afternoon to the Old Lord. On her way Chu Naima often stopped to breast-feed the baby. She seemed to have lost her sense of modesty and shyness, exposing her breasts to her charge at his demand — out in the open, in the playground and the courtyards. It embarrassed me to see Ming Ming twisting one of her nipples while mouthing the other. The male servants stopped and stared with open mouths at the pair of them. I, too, was somewhat stirred by the sight and had the impression that Ming Ming — and the Old Lord — regarded Chu Naima's breasts as playthings to squeeze for their milk, to fondle for their own pleasure until her two black nipples became swollen, red and erect; her breasts round and full. But I, sworn to a life of celibacy, would never have the chance to find out what Chu Naima experienced. From the expression on her face — as if in a trance — her eyes closed, mouth gaping, head tilted back, gasping movement of her throat, it was impossible to tell whether what she felt was secret pleasure, or immense pain.

Breast-feeding was a constant phenomenon with my mother, a common sight in my village, even our piglets tugged hungrily on the sow's breasts — and she seemed to have many more nipples than the human, enough for each of her eight piglets to have a go. It seemed appropriate and natural there, in the countryside, a necessity for sustaining the young. And I suddenly wondered how Gold had coped with her breasts engorged, congested with milk and no baby to suckle. Did the milk trickle away to waste in the nunnery, to the timing of the tock-tock-tock of the red wooden fish and the chant of the Buddhist script?

But in the House of Tang, breast-feeding took on a different connotation, amidst the surrounds of splendour and grandeur where Tai Tai was the central figure of sophistication and eroticism: shuffling along in her unsteady gait, her silk gown flowing, the gold and jade earrings dazzling, her ornamental hairpins of seed-pearls fluttering; the smooth texture of wood furniture with its intricate carvings and ornate mother-of-pearl insets shimmering, and the mesmeric odour of opium, the bejewelled and stoned Ancient Mistress. Here, even the commonplace transcended to a sensuous and exotic level.

'Our privileged wet nurse isn't very interested in her husband and her son any more, she ignored them during their monthly visit,' Tang Ma remarked.

'*Aiyah*, it's sad. She tried to breast-feed her son on his first visit, but he rejected her. Turned his face and cried.'

'She is now truly absorbed into the House of Tang, baby Ming Ming and the Old Lord are very dependent on her,' Tang Ma said.

'She really cares for Ming Ming, sleeps with him and breast-feeds him on demand,' Ho Ma remarked.

'She is very proud of Ming Ming, and carries him to show off to visitors at Tai Tai's *mah-jong* sessions. Ming Ming has replaced her own estranged son,' I said.

Among all the servants it was rumoured that Chu Naima was sleeping with the Old Lord.

'I have heard them laughing and giggling from his chambers,' the gardener claimed.

'*Aiyah*, she is so young, and not allowed to spend any time with her husband,' Ho Ma sympathised with her.

'The Old Lord was a playboy in his younger days. Old habits die hard,' the sedan-chair bearer testified. He had carried the Old Lord to the brothel and sing-song girls in his time.

I thought of Master, womanising in the brothel with the sing-song girls, and the time I had seen him mount and ride Tai Tai on that moonlit night. And whenever I heard the muffled protests and cries of the slave girls, I felt uneasy, frustrated, and I held on to the bolster, normally placed at the end of my bed. I clasped that long and round feathered pillow between my legs squeezing it tight and close until I felt a release, and fell asleep satisfied. Also, on the days preceding my 'horsy' there arose a strange sensation of fullness in my breasts, and in the secret darkness of the night, I fingered my nipples, squeezing them like Ming Ming did to Chu Naima's.

I kept this secret act to myself, for somehow I sensed that it was something improper, not 'chaste or virtuous' like watching the dogs in their intimacy.

But whenever I needed to gratify an inner urge I couldn't describe, I resorted to my comforter, my bolster, and I learned to ride it, rub it between my legs, imitating the motion of Master, faster and faster until I attained that release which washed away my tension and anxieties of the day. And I began to notice some coarse wiry hair at the bottom of my body just above my thighs, and also under my armpits, and during summer, there exuded an unpleasant smell of body odour as was common in my ancestral home, and I was ashamed of it. I secretly dabbed Tai Tai's rose-water or eau de Cologne to deodorise the areas under my arms.

More news came of killing and fighting in the north, always the mysterious north. At the *mah-jong* sessions I picked up snippets of conversations about the unrest going on outside the House of Tang.

'We're winning,' Mrs Sung declared. Everyone thought she had gamed, but she continued to play on, drawing another tile. 'My husband announced last night that Chiang Kai-shek has killed many Communists.'

Mrs Li joined in. 'But I heard from the men in my house that Chou En-lai managed to escape and he would surely return to revenge later on.'

'Didn't Sun Yat-sen die?' Tai Tai asked absent-mindedly.

'*Aiyah*, that's stale news, in 1925, two or three years ago. You're too cloistered in the House of Tang.'

'Nanking is now the capital, according to Chiang Kai-shek.'

'Huh, for how long I wonder? With all the fighting so uncertain, you win one day you lose another day.'

So Tai Tai and her three friends laughed while they exchanged news. We in the south were still unaffected by the fighting, and life went on as usual.

At Cole's New World, an enormous air-conditioned supermarket with tall shelves of displays, Kim is choosing a suitable bottle of food for Suchin from a range of Heinz baby products, there's a variety of meat — chicken, turkey, beef, lamb — and vegetables, and even desserts.

'Chicken a la King, spinach, and egg custard,' Kim reads while she picks three bottles. 'Best to let her try them out first, see how she likes them before buying any more.'

'*Aiyah*, how ingenous and convenient these days, such finely pureed food cooked and bottled, readily available and only needs warming up.'

I think of Ming Ming as he was at one year of age, teething: soft, and chubby wearing a triangular patchwork apron tied tightly around his tummy to curb his wind; he dribbled and loved to bite. Chu Naima introduced a soft diet which the chef cooked especially for him — minced chicken meat or liver, or pork, mashed carrots steamed with ground rice. And Chu Naima would first place the food in her own mouth, a spoonful at a time, softening it with her saliva, mushing it against the roof of her mouth, before regurgitating it to feed to Ming Ming in a spoon.

'That's how Ming Ming was fed, no convenient bottled Heinz baby puree . . .' I describe in detail to Kim.

'*Aiyah*, how unhygienic, eating the saliva of another person, what if she had a disease, like hepatitis?' Kim is shocked. 'Did you too feed me in this manner when I was small?'

'Your mother wouldn't permit it.'

'Thank God for that.' Then she comments, 'Although there's logic in it, the saliva is rich in digestive enzymes which break up the food, making it easier for the child to digest.'

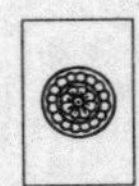

So the year went quickly, and the carpenters, painters, handy men came once again to prepare the house for the New Year. Tang Ma and Ho Ma returned one day with messages from Ah Han, asking me to invest the money I earned in gold, as the silver money and copper coins devalued day by day. So I told Tai Tai that I would like to use my wages to purchase some gold jewellery, and she instructed the goldsmith to design a fine gold necklace in pure twenty-four carat gold for me.

On that second New Year outing, Uncle Fatty Lee warned us: 'There are lots of thieves about. Be careful with your purses or jewellery.'

And we found that for the roadside shows the price of admission was at least a silver piece, and coppers were useless, and even the poor man's restaurant was no longer cheap as it had been the year before.

'My boss doesn't seem too optimistic about the wars,' Ah Han said.

'It's rumoured that the Kuomintang are winning, so that people don't panic, but in fact the Communists now have a new leader called Mao, the "hair" . . .'

'I too heard about this Mao who led the Autumn Harvest Uprising somewhere in the north. Trouble always starts in the north,' Uncle Fatty Lee said.

'The Mandarin says there's a lot of bribery and corruption going on at Customs, we've confiscated several consignments of opium, guns, and ammunition.'

'*Aiyah*, I heard that's only to make people believe his words, the Mandarin himself is also corrupted as the others.'

'No wonder,' Ah Yin said. 'They've received a lot of gifts from strangers lately, sent direct to the house.'

'So what's new in the House of Tang?' Ah Yin asked.

'Nothing much.'

'*Aiyah*, you must be the only one who doesn't know,' Uncle Fatty Lee said. 'Your Master is addicted to gambling, and now he's stealing the family antiques to sell, instead of going through your Tai Tai. The pawnbroker says so far it's only small items, maybe still unnoticed by the family.'

'I know that Tai Tai grumbles about the sharp rise in price of opium from the black market.'

On my return to the House of Tang I was again severed from all the troubles of the outside world, political, martial and financial. The routine of the household resumed in its usual leisurely way, without interruption or interference. The children attended classes, Tai Tai her *mah-jong* session, the Ancient Mistress her opium; the Old Lord and Ming Ming had their wet nurse, and Master the slaves. We, the servants, held our gossip cum hair-combing sessions as usual, our topics usually confined to the events of the household, for we knew little else.

I remember very well the day Mrs Sung arrived for the *mah-jong* session and excitedly announced: 'The Kuomintangs, the Nationalists, have taken Peking, and now call it 'Peiping' (Northern peace).'

Tang Ma said it was the year of the Dragon — 1928. The Dragon represented imperialism, and this city was destined later to become the official capital of the People's Republic of China — Beijing.

'Time's swift like an arrow' was a cliche our village storyteller used to indicate a time leap in his stories: so my time in the House of Tang flew like an arrow. Countless days and nights merged and passed, months came and went, seasons changed, and festivals were celebrated as before. And on the second day of each New Year, I went out with Uncle Fatty Lee, Ah Sai and my three sisters.

Ming Ming was five years old when we heard the terrible news of the Japanese invasion of Manchuria, and of the puppet-government they had set up under Pu Yi.

Mrs Li, the naval officer's wife, informed us: 'Chiang Kai-shek, who was expecting international help, was disappointed, and forced to accept a truce.'

In the government department, the high officials were planning their migration.

'We're packing our personal effects to freight to Hong Kong, for we never know when we might have to flee.'

Later that year, when we went out on the New Year outing, the streets of Canton were full of refugees from the north. The scenes of the exodus I had witnessed in my village repeated themselves, great mobs of people moving, by rickshaws, by bullock-carts, by motor-cars and trucks, bicycles, on foot, heading south to Hong Kong.

Tai Tai's *mah-jong* games started to become irregular. The army and the navy chiefs and their families had orders to stand by, get ready to move at a moment's notice; and many a time false alarms were issued, and the Sung and Li families were in disarray. Ah Han and Ah Fong planned to move with their bosses to Hong Kong, and sent messages to me through Tang Ma and Ho Ma, their forwarding addresses written on a slip of paper. Tang Ma was told that Ah Yin's boss would move later, in a year or two, because he was in the civil service and in no great hurry.

Our final New Year outing all together took place in the year of the Dog — 1934. We went out, each with a heavy heart, knowing that soon some of us would be leaving Canton and that we would be separated from each other, our days full of uncertainties. And the roadside shows had deteriorated, there were no more mirrors, and the freaks and animals weren't there.

Ah Han said: 'I hear something supposed to be confidential. The Communists have started on a long march towards the mountainous regions in the west, and many have perished on the way, but are reinforced by other Communist groups.'

'And they have declared war on the Japanese,' Ah Fong said.

Tai Tai's *mah-jong* sessions ceased altogether after the first month of the New Year. But she had visitors from Shanghai, the famous transvestite opera singer, MeiLan Fong, and his musicians. They too were fleeing to Hong Kong, and stayed at the House of Tang to entertain Tai Tai while waiting for the rest of the troupe to arrive from the north.

At a hair-combing session one morning, it was time to pluck and shape each other's eyebrows. We used a single strand of white cotton twined round the thumb and fore-fingers of each hand, and with a swift scissor action, we extracted the fine hair of the brow, without much pain.

That morning Tang Ma softly broke the news to me: 'Ah Han and Ah Fong have left with their bosses' families for Hong Kong. Two days ago, when we met in the bazaar, they said goodbye.'

'What about the Wu family, where Ah Yin is working?'

'Oh they're still here, Mr Wu is still taking as many bribes as he can before he leaves. Ah Yin is well, I only spoke to the male chef yesterday.'

I was sorry to hear that Ah Han and Ah Fong had gone, and felt quite forlorn. That night I cried myself to sleep thinking of my two sisters in Hong Kong, and of Ah Yin by herself. Ah Sai, my baby brother, had grown more estranged from me each year. When I met him he wouldn't utter a sentence, answering my questions in monosyllables.

The following year Ah Yin left with the Wus for Hong Kong, and Tang Ma said some messengers had sent word from Ah Han to say that she and Ah Fong were well and were seeing each other, and that Ah Yin had arrived safe and sound. They said that I should try to join them in Hong Kong as soon as I could. Tai-Tai was waiting for the other three Masters' decision, as the accountant had already written to them overseas, to advise moving the business to Hong Kong, or somewhere else in south-east Asia. He advised that the estate should be sold, and migration seriously considered in view of the civil and Sino-Japanese wars spreading in China.

It was early afternoon, a sweltering summer day. A loud shriek shook the stillness of the air.

'Help — save a life. *Lai ren lah*.'

Again the cry rang through the courtyard, from the direction of the east wing, the residence of the Old Lord.

'Isn't it Chu Naima?'

'Help — save a life. *Lai ren lah*.'

'Sounds like Chu Naima's voice,' I again told Tai Tai at her siesta.

'Go and see what's going on,' she ordered.

The gardener, Ah Chan and Tang Ma were racing across the Garden of Eternal Tranquility. But I was the first to dash into the room, pushing the door wide open. I saw Naima Chu astride the Old Lord, who was lying on a bed. She was slapping his face.

'Wake up, wake up,' she cried, frantically.

She turned round, face stricken with terror. Her chest was bare, both breasts full and dangling, streams of milk leaking from the nipples. Her pants were down to the ankles.

The Old Lord wore a stiff smile, eyes fixed in a mischievous stare. His lower jaw gaped open, dribbling milk. His genitalia was exposed: a shrivelled penis, and balls dry and black like two pickled olives.

'Died in the act of copulation,' the gardener said.

'Too strenuous for him. A heart attack,' was the verdict of the sedan-chair bearer.

'What a blissful way to die,' said Ah Chan his servant, full of envy.

'He was about to come,' Chu Naima explained in between her sobs. And instinctively I knew that the Old Lord must have tried to mount or ride Chu Naima, and that the exertion had proved too much for him and cost him his life. Rejuvenation by breast-feeding indeed. Breast-feeding had only rekindled his lust.

Tang Ma and I helped Chu Naima get off the bed, buttoned up her tunic and pulled up her pants to tie at the waist with a sash. The cook brought her a hot chicken broth laced with brandy to calm her nerves.

Ah Chan worked to restore some respectability in the Old Lord, before rigor mortis set in. He pulled his eyelids over the eyes, forcibly closed his lower jaw, with his dentures in place. With a wet towel he wiped the Old Lord's mouth, and fingers — still wet and smelling of vaginal fragrance — and arranged his arms at his sides. Then he plaited his thin grey hair.

The Old Lord's body could not be allowed to reveal what he had been doing when he died, especially at his ripe age of ninety-five. He would be the laughing stock of Canton, most unbecoming for the rich and reputable House of Tang. Dignity had to be restored before the Taoist priest came to administer his last rites.

The Ancient Mistress was in a stupor and Master was too drunk to appreciate the meaning of this death for the family. So Tai Tai and the accountant conferred, to plan the wake and the funeral.

First the other three Masters who were overseas had to be notified. It was mandatory for them to return for the funeral and burial.

Ah Chan went to the post office to send them 'electrical notices'.

'Very fast rate please,' he requested.

'It's very expensive.'

'Expense doesn't matter, the Old Lord is dead.'

Twenty-four hours later, three replies came from three different countries: America, Australia and England. All three Masters and their families would be arriving home in three days time through the 'empty air' by the 'flying machine'.

A white cloth was hung across the main front gate of the House of Tang, and a white lantern on each side of the door, with the Old Lord's name, a summary of his good deeds, and his age written on them. He became three years older upon his death, ninety-eight instead of ninety-five.

'One age for the heavens, one for the earth, and one for man. Longevity is a blessing, so it's a pride to show that he has lived a long life,' Tang Ma explained.

Kim has received an invitation to attend an old Chinese lady's birthday banquet in Chinatown. She says: 'She's eighty years old, born in Canton, came from China like you.'

I advise her: 'The eighty birthday is considered as the grand birth, you must wear red, and must wish her many blessings for a long life:
"longevity as high as the southern mountain
luck as deep as the eastern ocean".'

'In Western culture they say only the good die young,' Kim says.

'Nonsense, but even the Australians wish you many happy

returns at your birthday party, it's the same token.'

After my visit to the Chinese nursing home in Earlwood I have doubts about the old Chinese concept of longevity being a blessing and a pride. In practice I see it as a burden to others, in nursing, caring, medical treatment, and the cost to the Australian government in subsidies and welfare. I have no idea how old my father was when he died, only that he never woke up from his sleep after drinking the brewed herbs from the physician. I have always thought that was a blessing, as it cut short his suffering from the 'galloping consumption'.

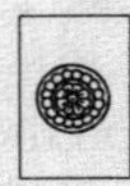

All members of the House of Tang went into mourning. The Ancient Mistress, Masters, and their families, all wore sack gowns and headgears of sacks and shoes of straw. The distant relatives wore white, and all the servants and slaves wore black. The ladies shed their gold jewellery and coloured ribbons, and let their hair down and loose.

The Old Lord's coffin had been waiting to receive him for the past thirty-four years. It was a present given to him by his four sons on his sixty-first birthday; and was kept in the antechamber of his bedroom, so it would not be far for him to be carried.

The hardwood coffin and lid was carved from one whole log of wood, imported from Lui Chow. It was carved like a boat, and well polished, to facilitate the Old Lord's smooth passage through Hell to the next incarnated world.

Professional wailers were hired for nine days. They sat surrounding the coffin, and would cry and wail when friends and relatives came to pay their respect. The wake lasted through the night. In the day, long tedious ceremonies were conducted by the Taoist priest, and the musicians played eerie mournful music. The Old Lord's daughter-in-law, the Ancient Mistress, his two daughters, the four granddaughters-in-law, and great-granddaughters sat at the head of his corpse.

The women would cry out now and again, beating their chests. It was a show of grief and lamentation for the deceased, who they would normally depend upon for help and favours, and a demonstration of how they would miss him now that he had departed. But women used this as an excuse to air their personal grievances, to bemoan publicly whatever injustices they had been subjected to for all present to hear. For women in those days were prohibited to speak up in the presence of men, whether they be their fathers, brothers, or husbands; they were expected to speak only when spoken to. So women could only gossip among themselves, telling their troubles and worries to each other. The ululation at the wake was the only time in their lives when they could be heard in public, the only time to show that they had a voice.

'*Aiyah*, Old Lord, take me with you. No use my remaining here like a cripple with my bound feet, can't even go out to the opera,' Tai Tai complained.

One of his daughters sobbed aloud. 'My mother-in-law treated me like a slave, I had to cook and wash dishes, because I couldn't produce a male child for that family . . .'

The Ancient Mistress, his one and only daughter-in-law cried: 'Yesterday they tried to ration my opium. Too expensive they said. My only pleasure denied, I would rather die then go without my opium. Oh Old Lord, take me with you.'

The corpse was adorned with rings and bracelets made of

gold, jade and pearl. It was believed that jade and pearl prevented the body from decay. A silver coin was placed in the Old Lord's mouth, clamped in between his dentures. Such was the custom of the rich. The women paid for the layers of paper coverlets inscribed with the character of longevity in bluish-green ink which were placed over the corpse.

The old Chinese believe that when a man dies he has three spirits: one would remain at the grave, one at the altar of the ancestors' tablet, and the other would wander off to Yellow Springs, and for that reason, to make his stay in Yellow Springs comfortable, paper mould of gold ingot, paper effigy of male servant and slaves and a wet-nurse, a house and few sedan-chairs were burnt for his requirements in the next world, before the reincarnation.

A Taoist priest specialising in funerals was consulted for an auspicious day for the funeral and burial. After casting a horoscope he predicted that on the seventh day the departed spirit would return home for a visit. That evening all the doors and windows in the House of Tang were left open. A large moth flew in and settled in the Old Lord's room. We whispered in low voices that this moth was his spirit, when the candles were suddenly blown out by a puff of wind.

The Old Lord was buried in the family burial ground next to his wife who had departed some twenty years before him. The pall-bearers and the mourners did not have far to go, as it was right at the back of the walled-in complex, behind the servants' quarters, the vegetable patch and the enclosure of domestic animals, beyond the shrubs and bushes, where the ground was slightly elevated and had a distant view of the north and west branches of the Pearl River. Good *feng shui* so that future generations would prosper.

After the burial, the accountant was summoned before the family to disclose the will.

'It's the Old Lord's will that the house, land and business be divided into six shares, one for his daughter-in-law, the Ancient Mistress, one for each of his four grandsons, and one for Ming Ming, the first son from his number-one grandson the Master.'

'What about us?' his two daughters asked.

'Nothing for daughters, their dowries were the only inheritance they received.'

'Most unfair the way women are treated,' they grumbled.

Before the two daughters left for their homes, they ordered the servants to loot the antiques. They gathered up china, vases, scrolls of painting and calligraphy from the Old Lord's room and the reception hall and carried them away.

Tai Tai came to intercept them, and a quarrel ensued. 'These belonged to *my* father, we have a right to them.'

The three Masters from overseas also demanded their share of assets to be converted into foreign currency and remitted overseas.

Master continued to steal antiques and jewellery to pay for his gambling debts and revelry at the brothels. The Ancient Mistress was too drugged by opium to guard her belongings but Tai Tai had hidden her valuables, and had Jade and I stand guard at her door.

When the rest of the troup of MeiLan Fong finally arrived, they were in a great hurry to leave for Hong Kong. The two new arrivals were sing-song girls of great fame in Shanghai. They told us that transportation was getting very difficult as hundreds of thousands of people were trying to leave Shanghai.

'Stay awhile please,' Tai Tai urged them.

They declined. 'Things are really bad up north, because of the Xian incident.'

We looked ignorant, having been busy with the funeral and the quarrelling about the estate.

'*Aiyah*, haven't you heard? Chiang Kai-shek was kidnapped at Huaquing Hotspring . . .'

'When?'

'Last month. He's alive though.'

It was 1936 — the year of the humble Rat — and the bad news made Tai Tai decide it was time to migrate, and to sell the House of Tang.

The House of Tang was auctioned and sold to a warlord, the proceeds divided, and the family dispersed. The three Masters returned with their families to their homes overseas.

'We too must pack and leave this mansion before the month is up, as the new owner will take possession of the place,' Tai Tai announced.

I asked Tai Tai for permission to go out with Uncle Fatty Lee for a day, as I had to pay the *siasin lao* in the bazaar to write me a letter informing Ah Han in Hong Kong of my arrival date. The *siasin lao* charged two pieces of silver, and he advised me: 'You better get rid of the Chinese money if you're going to Hong Kong, as there a different currency is used, that of the British system.'

So I appointed another day with Tai Tai's permission to go to the bank with Uncle Fatty Lee to change my Chinese money, but there were long queues everywhere, and a friend of Uncle Fatty Lee suggested we try the pawnshop, where I converted my Chinese money into some portable assets: a silver waist watch on a chain for Ah Sai and a pair of Ming rice-bowls for myself. With the money that remained I bought silver pieces and wrapped them in red-packets to give to Uncle Fatty Lee and Ah Sai on the day of my departure.

'They're called silver pieces, but are made of nickel, an inferior metal,' the pawnbroker said.

It was a month of chaos and dislocation, of sorting, selecting and discarding things unwanted or redundant, of deciding whether to keep for the intrinsic value or for sentimental reason.

The servants were given a choice — to stay on with the family of Tang or to leave them and seek work elsewhere.

Pearl and Ruby wrecked Master's bedroom and ornaments, before they fled to join a subversive group.

'They turned Communists,' the gardener observed. 'They went off with the young speaker at the street corner exhorting people to join the Communist army.'

Jade was the loyal one who stayed on with Tai Tai.

Streams of refugees passed through Canton, fleeing south, to Hong Kong, Annam (Vietnam), Burma, India, Malaya. The government officials themselves were planning to migrate to Formosa (Taiwan), Hawaii, the United States.

Tai Tai received letters from the Sung and the Li families exhorting her to go to Formosa, a safe retreat, away from the Japanese and the Communists, and she decided to go where her friends were. I received a letter from Ah Han, which Tai Tai read to me, which said that my sisters would be at the wharf to receive me on the day of my expected arrival in Hong Kong.

The faithful servants — Tang Ma, Ho Ma, Jade, Peach and Peony, Ah Chan and Ah Wai, the gardeners and their wives — all vowed to stay with the Tang family. Not so Chu Naima, the privileged wet-nurse. She had quietly slipped away in the chaos. Her rickshaw-puller husband collected her and the trunks of treasures she had pillaged from the House of Tang, deserting Ming Ming whom she had cared for as her own for ten years.

The House of Tang moved *en masse*. All antique ornate furniture, Ming and Ching vases and porcelain wares, scrolls of calligraphy and painting, were carefully and professionally packed. Hand-woven silk carpets, embroidered sheets, drapes for commemoration of birthdays and weddings, tablets of ancestor worship, were stored in camphor trunks.

Domestic animals from the enclosure behind the servants' quarters — pigs, cows, goats, chickens, ducks, geese — were led two by two up the plank into the hold of the freighter S.S. *SeaKiang*, normally used for exporting dried seafood, with a few cabins for passengers. Even live fish — carp, perches, groupa — came aboard in large tanks.

The gardeners transplanted vegetables, fruits, tubers in portable pots, and salvaged as many pots and bowls of bonsai, cumquat, and blossoming flowers as they could. 'We have taken many varieties of pods and seeds to plant in the new country,' they told me.

I had gained two large trunks of clothes, lovely embroidered pillowcases, bedspreads, and sheets which had been discarded. Tai Tai had personally rewarded me with a pair of jade earrings set in gold and a large oval jade ring. She also gave me a letter of introduction to work for her friend in Hong Kong.

I wanted a passage in the freighter as far as Hong Kong, where Han, Fong and Yin were waiting for me. The six sedan-chair bearers and their wives also wanted to go to Hong Kong, for they had heard that they could make a good living there in the rickshaw business.

Uncle Fatty Lee and Ah Sai came to the wharf to see me off.

Uncle Fatty Lee had aged a lot during the ten years I had been in Canton, but it was Ah Sai who had really changed. He was now fourteen, tall, lanky and very self-assured and independent. He seemed a stranger to me, his only surviving sister. Was it because we had only seen each other once a year? In the process of growing up we each seemed to have gone our own separate secret way; despite the blood tie between us, we were estranged. Severed. I had been too cloistered, and he too exposed in the city of Canton, we had lived in two totally different worlds — one of splendour, the other of squalor.

'What's the point of going to a new place at my age?' Uncle Fatty Lee said to me. 'I cannot adapt to a strange country, besides all my friends are here. Come what may, I'll look after Ah Sai.'

'Be careful, Ah Sai, look after yourself and obey Uncle Fatty Lee, work hard. Uncle Fatty Lee could trace me through sister Ah Han, keep in touch. If I get a chance I'll buy you a passage to come down to Hong Kong and then we'll be together again.'

Ah Sai nodded but spoke not a word, and didn't even want to clasp my hands.

We waved. I cried. Men weren't supposed to cry. 'Men shed blood not tears' is another common wise saying in Chinese. Men aren't softies, they're tough, even if they're sad they won't cry in public; they'll cry in silence, alone at night in their bed. I hoped Ah Sai would be all right, would understand the reasons for my leaving him.

As the S.S. *SeaKiang* entered the estuary of the Pearl River, the sun was sinking in the horizon between the sea and the sky. As the river mouth widened, our ship moved away from other vessels. The colour of the water changed from muddy silty yellow into the purer blue of the ocean. Gone was the musty oily stench of the Pearl River. Instead a fresh sea breeze carried with it the faint taste of salty sprays. Soon the whole scene was engulfed in darkness, save for the twinkling of stars and the flickering lights of distant ships. The droning of the ship's engine and the lapping of waves broke the silence of the night.

Hong Kong

ON THE MORNING OF MY arrival, I watched from my porthole as a veil of mist slowly lifted to reveal my first glimpse of Hong Kong — Xiangang, the Fragrant Harbour — in early dawn. Victoria Harbour. Bustling with ocean-liners, warships, junks, ferries, wallah-wallahs, each sounding the blast of foghorns. In the distance a clocktower stood against the silhouette of hills, closer to the waterfront were buildings with verandahs on the second storeys. Pedestrians jostled on the footpaths: Chinese men with long pigtails, in traditional costumes of side-slitted tunics and pants, or the westernised ones with hair cut short and plastered behind their ears, wearing shirt, jacket and tie. And so many foreigners, the *feng kwei lao*, with red moustache and green eyes. The streets were crammed with vehicles: the 'gas fume' cars, rickshaws, and trams with antennae which ran on tracks in the centre of the road.

The steward sounded a gong to summon those of us who wanted to disembark in Hong Kong to the dining-room for an early breakfast, as we had to be ready for the inspection by the quarantine and custom officers. I sat at the table with the sedan-chair bearers and their families, and we were served congee and fried fritters by uniformed stewards, who also waited on us.

Then Tang Ma appeared to inform us that Ancient Mistress, Master and Tai Tai were waiting to bid us farewell in the ballroom. They were seated near the stage at the far end of the ballroom, with their respective slaves and man servants behind them. Each sedan-chair bearer and his family knelt and kowtowed to the three bosses, and thanked them for the privilege of working for them, and for housing and feeding the whole family. They said they would remember always the House of Tang with eternal gratitude, and wished them all a long healthy life, and continued prosperity. The wives and children howled and cried, and Tang Ma handed out to each a red-packet of good luck money and reciprocated their best wishes, on behalf of the bosses.

When my turn came, which was last, I had already shed a lot of tears, and I felt guilty to be leaving Tai Tai, and begged her to forgive my desertion, as I had vowed 'sisters' to look after. I exhorted Jade, whose eyes were red with sadness, to take good care of Tai Tai and to attend to her foot-care daily, as I had been doing for the past ten years. The Ancient Mistress and the Master were getting bored, and I could see Ancient Mistress's withdrawal symptoms becoming more obvious, so I turned to all the other servants to wish them good health and longevity, and expressed my appreciation especially to Tang Ma, Ho Ma, and Wu Ma, for their friendship and company.

Then we were dragged away, torn from the family of Tang, as the custom officials had been waiting and were getting impatient. It was heart-rending to leave them after a decade of living together. And again I felt remorse and regrets, and wanted to change my mind, to stay with them, to go wherever they were going, Formosa, now known as Taiwan, or even to America . . . I'd spent ten years with them, from the age of fourteen to twenty-four, they were closer to me than my sworn sisters with whom I had only spent about twelve days in all, in my whole life.

But Tang Ma urged me firmly: 'You've sworn an oath, it should be honoured and taken seriously. Already your three sisters have been waiting in Hong Kong for two to three years for you to join them, and are looking forward to receiving you at the wharf.'

Tai Tai gave me an envelope with the address of her friend in Hong Kong to whom she had highly recommended me. 'She'll take good care of you, treat you like her companion, I know,' she said. Her six daughters and their *naimas* were also sorry to see us go.

'Study hard in your new country,' I advised them.

Tai Tai said: 'I hope to send them to the American 'big schools' later on, their generation is very lucky indeed to have such opportunities.'

'In life we separate; in death we finally part' is another saying in Chinese, meaning separation is only temporary, there's still hope of a reunion or chance meeting later in life. Death is a definite division of our body from its soul.

The steamer dropped anchor at Victoria Harbour, and all of us who were disembarking boarded little putt-putt boats to reach the pier.

From afar I saw my three sisters at the pier, with their pigtails and white tunics and black pants, among a crowd of strangers, Chinese and foreigners. Ah Han instructed two coolies to carry my trunks and baggage in a 'gas fumed' cart, and the four of us rode in two rickshaws to the guest house where I was to stay for the night.

My sisters were given special leave for the day by their boss — they all worked for the same family now, Taipan of the Taikoo Hong fame. After I'd stored my luggage in my room, we went out for lunch. And I was filled with the excitement of arrival in a new place, the thrill of adventure. We roamed through crowds of pedestrians and passed rows of shop-houses, three or four storeys high, and finally entered a restaurant. It was packed and noisy, and we stood behind some customers at a table, ready to rush for their seats as soon as they showed signs of leaving. I was being exposed to the outside world — people were aggressive and pushy.

I showed Ah Han the address of Tai Tai's friend.

'Well give it a trial for a week at least, and if you're not happy, ring these numbers, let me know. So easy to get jobs here,' she said.

I couldn't understand her. 'How to ring these numbers? I can't read any of them.'

'*Aiyah*, you peasant. This is the "electric-talkie" number. You turn a crank and ask the operator to connect you to these numbers, and you will hear my voice when I answer, and we can talk through it.'

'You mean I can talk to you from a distance?'

'There's a mouth-piece which you talk into, and an ear-piece you hold close to your ear to listen,' Yin explained. And she mimed with her hands.

The other two laughed. 'Where have you been hiding all these years? Far behind time.'

A country bumpkin indeed. Wide-eyed with excitement in a modern city. There were many things here that I had missed out on in Canton. I was bewildered and baffled by Hong Kong, so advanced and fascinating. The 'self-come' water that spurted out from a tap, the 'self-come' light that came on by tugging a long cord, the toilet which flushed by pulling a chain from a cistern. And the electric tram with two long antennae, without animals or people pulling. I was glad I had left Canton. I felt liberated from the barriers of high walls and hedges. My world had expanded to include sea, sky, hills. A new land and city for me to explore.

My place of work had swung from one extreme to another. From the enormous complex of the House of Tang with more than fifty occupants, to an apartment of about thirty by twenty feet confined within four walls, without any garden or courtyard.

Hong Kong was where I first encountered little steps leading from one narrow street to another, and in the houses too: stairs, spiral fire ladder, smooth wooden-turned baluster, cast-iron railings, 'electric stairway' like a large bird-cage to facilitate transport from one level to another.

My new mistress, Little Peacock Lien, looked very familiar.

'So you've arrived safely. I had a telephone call from your Tai Tai about you. She is sailing today, heading for Formosa first, but the final destination is still uncertain, maybe America later on,' she said.

Then I remembered she had been one of the two sing-song girls who had fled from Shanghai to join the MeiLan Fong troupe, the ones who had brought news of the Xian incident. She had been shabbily dressed then, dirty and thin, her hair tucked under a scarf. Now she was attired in a Chinese side-slit silk dress, a *cheongsam* with a stand up collar which showed off her hourglass figure and her slender legs. On her face, shaped like a duck's egg, she wore heavy make-up; but the most attractive features were her two dark eyes which seemed to penetrate me, reading my inner thoughts.

'You'll be my handmaid, chaperon, and also help Au Ma, the cook, with the general house-chores.'

Little Peacock Lien's apartment, or 'single space' as the locals called it, was on the fourth floor of a five-storey block. On each floor there were six such apartments accessible from a long corridor. The 'electric stairway' conveyed the passengers between floors. Its door folded aside like a fan. Its descent was unsteady; the ascent shaky. It would rattle, shake, and jerk to a sudden stop.

I shared a bunk bed with Au Ma in the servants' room. I slept on the upper bunk, with a base of wooden planks, topped with a smooth woven mat. Our room was next to the toilet and kitchen. It had no window and was dark, even in the daytime. The kitchen was part of a balcony which looked out into an air-well, where bamboo poles were cantilevered out for hanging clothes. There was a trellis floor to catch any fallen clothes from the poles. In the bathroom there was a number of urns containing water, some for bathing, washing, some in special filtering containers.

'Water is precious here, as it comes from China in pipes, and is rationed,' Au Ma told me. 'It's available from the tap only for four hours each day, and during this period we should try to store as much as water as possible for a whole day's use. Some families take their clothes to Macau by boat to be washed there, Macau is part of the continuity of China whereas Hong Kong is an island.' So I guessed it was because Hong Kong, being a small island with houses so congested together, had no land left for digging wells.

Au Ma was about my height. She was the most serious looking person I'd ever come across, modestly dressed in a white tunic and black pants. Her chignon was flat and big like a pancake stuck to the back of her head.

'Are you a "comb-up" too?' I asked.

'No, I'm married, but have no children and my husband and I didn't get on too well, so I came out to work. Have been here for more than half a year.'

She spoke softly and cautiously, as though weighing every word for its significance before speaking. She reminded me a little of Wu Ma, Gold's companion of the month.

Generally my job was to carry out the orders of Little Peacock Lien, and to help Au Ma. Unlike in Canton, where I was allowed out only once a year, here I went out at least twice a day. But always in the company of my mistress or Au Ma.

The first night Au Ma whispered to me: 'Little Peacock Lien is a black-market mistress, kept by a very rich business man, Mr Xi, who visits her regularly once a week.'

'Black-market? You mean he had to buy her illegally?'

'No, he already has a wife at home, she's a secret mistress, that's what black-market means, his wife doesn't know about his affair.'

'In the houses of Canton a wife and concubines can live together, and my previous Master slept with the slave girls with the full knowledge of Tai Tai, there was no need for secrecy.'

'*Aiyah*, here in Hong Kong we're governed by the British, the law is different, it's strictly one man one wife.'

'The legality of "one man one wife" doesn't stop the man from taking other women then?'

'Obviously not, but a kept mistress by a rich person is very common practice, and it's not a secure proposition, for when the man is tired of the same woman he can always leave her and get another. He can't leave his legal wife that easily, for marriage by law is signing a contract, and its dissolution has to be legal, with an application to the court of law.' Au Ma sighed. 'Huh, any woman from good family wouldn't be seen in public as a sing-song girl by choice, no female of good breeding wants to "expose her head and reveal her face" as the saying goes, except by force of circumstances.'

And I began to feel sorry for Little Peacock Lien, for being in such an involvement, and I wished I could give her some advice as to how to prepare herself for the day when she would fall out of grace with Mr Xi, and would be stripped of all this glamour, perhaps this house and both of us servants.

So I secretly nursed a prejudice against Mr Xi even before I met him. In my mind he was a coward, a thief, cheating behind his wife's back.

But Mr Xi's visit was the highlight of the week. He came on a Wednesday, for about four or five hours, in the afternoon. He never stayed overnight.

'Wouldn't dare to, in case his wife starts questioning him,' Au Ma said. 'Under her thumb.'

'Hen-pecked by her,' I said.

'She must be a very powerful or aggressive woman, must nag and cry and make lots of noise. Mr Xi can't bear any such scenes and is afraid of fierce woman.'

'Or perhaps he is afraid of "losing face" if news of quarrels should leak out.'

To the Chinese, preservation of 'face' or self-dignity is of paramount importance, especially in domestic affairs. Any disharmony is hushed up, so as not to 'lose face.'

Early on Wednesday mornings I would accompany Au Ma to the market to buy food: a live chicken, a pigeon or a flapping fish. And from her fastidious method, I learned how to pick a fleshy but not fat chicken, a meaty pigeon, and fresh tender young green vegetables. We would spend hours going from stall to stall, finally ending at her favourite hawker, bargaining and haggling. Au Ma was an expert at slaughtering chickens, slitting their throats and plucking feathers, scooping out entrails. The meat would be double-steamed in lidded containers with ginseng or bird's nest, or herbs of tonic value. My task was to pick fine debris, like tiny feathers, from a bowl of dried bird's nest immersed and softened in water. I learned to prepare Mr Xi's favourite tea of *lung ching* (Dragon well) adding a few dragon-eye fruits, the logans.

'Mr Xi has been working hard all day,' Little Peacock Lien would say. 'He needs to drink something with a cooling effect.'

Kim has a sore throat and persistent cough.

'*Aiyah*, you mustn't eat the Kentucky Fried Chicken too often, such deep-fried meat in batter is too "heaty". I'll make you some chrysanthemum tea to cool you down.'

'I'll get some antibiotics, I think I'm getting a fever; it's the flu at this time of the year.'

'Always taking those antibiotics, too dispersive, bad for your system.'

'You call this hot tea "cooling"?'

'It's got nothing to do with the temperature of the food, it's the effect it has on the body.'

'On what scientific basis do you tell what is "heaty" and what is cooling?'

'Some foodstuff is classified as "heaty" and some as "cooling". I'm illiterate, I can't read or tell you how it's done. I just know that watermelon, for instance, is "cooling" and will calm and purify the body system; fried things are "heaty" and will cause sore throat.'

Kim says: 'It's all guesswork, no scientific back-up for it, just like the so-called meridians, those imaginary lines in acupuncture treatment. Sore throat is caused by a germ.'

'A practice of hundreds of years, treatment for millions of Chinese, must have some truth, as it does have good effects.'

Kim shrugs her shoulders. Whenever she's uncertain she does that.

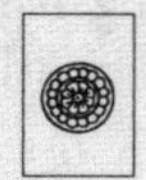

After returning from the market, I chaperoned Little Peacock Lien to the hairdressing salon. I stood at a discreet distance, watching her being shampooed. I admired the way her fringe was curled with red-hot tongs, and how her long hair was plaited and swirled into twin chignons, secured and adorned with fresh fragrant jasmine.

On returning home, often too excited to eat, she would settle for a bowl of steamed bird's nest soup for lunch and she would dress in pink — Mr Xi's favourite colour. She took a long time to do her make-up, applying her face with liquid powder and using a small sheet of red paper to colour her lips and cheeks red. I helped her dab essence of sandalwood on her wrists, her neck, and behind her ears.

'Not too much, Mr Xi is allergic to perfume,' she said. 'Just enough to dispel body odour, I don't want poor Mr Xi sneezing and sniffing away.'

Au Ma tidied the lounge, the bedroom, put out clean

towels and sheets. I dusted shelves and tables with a feather duster, and arranged flowers in vases.

When Mr Xi rang the doorbell, Au Ma answered the door, and took his English hat and jacket to hang. My role was to announce loudly, 'Mistress, Mr Xi has arrived', and to fetch his silk slippers.

Little Peacock Lien, radiant with smiles, came to greet him. '*Aiyah nee lai ler*.' An expression of pleasure on receiving a dear friend.

The Chinese don't hug or kiss or even hold hands in public. Not proper. Such immoral behaviour is frowned upon.

For a minute they stood speechless, gazing with adoration into each other's eyes. Then Mr Xi would settle himself in his comfortable chair while I placed his slippers by his feet. Little Peacock Lien herself would help him take off his shoes and prop his feet up on a pouffe. 'You must have had an exhausting day,' she exclaimed.

Mr Xi had his hair cut short, western style, thick and black, plastered down, shining with brilliantine. He stood about five feet four, the same height as Little Peacock Lien, but was stout and stocky. His broad face was set with small features: small elevated nose, small even white teeth. His small eyes were beady, slit-like, suggestively sly and scheming. He stared at me from head to foot and said to Little Peacock Lien, 'So this is your new servant Ah Silver?'

'Yes, Mr Xi, please drink tea,' I said, as instructed by Au Ma. I fetched his hot tea with the logans in an exquisite Ching teacup with lid and I offered it to him with both hands.

Mr Xi had a great sense of humour, and he brought life into our apartment, with his jokes, yarns, anecdotes, gossip and news. Au Ma and I stood listening, on either side of their chairs, as part of the audience. Little Peacock Lien's laughter and applause rang through the house.

Then it was her turn to entertain him, with a song she had just learned or a tune played on the lute. And Mr Xi tried to sing along, but was terribly out of key. I suppressed my giggles, and Au Ma rolled her eyes.

After dinner, we prepared Mr Xi's bath. Au Ma boiled hot water, which I transferred into a large earthen urn in the bathroom as only cold water was available from the tap. While Mr Xi and Little Peacock Lien retired to the bedroom for their rest, Au Ma and I ate the leftovers in the kitchen. They always left the eyes of the fish for me to eat, believing they would strengthen my drooping eyelid.

About six or seven o'clock, Mr Xi and Little Peacock Lien would emerge from the bedroom. Mr Xi checked and rechecked his appearance in the mirror in the sitting-room, adjusting his hair and his hat. His parting words were always the same: 'Learn well from the master, perfect your technique, there's great potential in your voice and talent . . .' And to Au Ma and me, he said: 'Look after your mistress well, don't be lazy.' And he would hand us our salary or tips, and leave a wad of notes for Little Peacock Lien by her bedside table.

Our life revolved around Mr Xi. We depended on him for our livelihood. He was our god who made all things possible with that magic commodity — money. The morning after his visit was always a deflation: empty, quiet, and dull. Little Peacock Lien hid in her room and cried.

Au Ma whispered to me that Mr Xi and Little Peacock Lien were very much in love. When I went marketing with Au Ma she would tell me about Little Peacock Lien.

'She's only nineteen years old, younger than you, but she must have gone through a lot of hardship.'

'Mr Xi looks old enough to be her father.'

'*Aiyah*, he's thirty years older, forty-nine this year. But they seem very much in love, every day she's sitting by the phone waiting for him to call, and if he doesn't call her, she cries herself to sleep.'

On days when they did not see each other, I'd seen her waiting patiently for his call on the 'electric talkie'.

'Why can't she call him, so easy to do on the "electric talkie." I had dialled and spoken to my three sisters several times already, at least once a week.

'She is not allowed to reciprocate his calls. Not convenient he said. He doesn't want his wife to know. Even his office staff cannot be trusted. Next time he visits just try to see how he comes up.'

I paid attention on Mr Xi's next visit, and sure enough he came up the fire-exit spiral stairway. He didn't want to be seen either in the bird-cage elevator or the public staircase through the corridor. Just like a thief, stealthy and cryptic.

The rest of the week was rather routine. Little Peacock Lien was taking singing and lute lessons on alternate days of the week except on Wednesday. She practised her singing very early in the morning, 'at the first crow of the cock' as advised by her master, while the voice was still fresh from a night's rest, unadulterated by drinks, food or smoke.

At nine o'clock promptly MeiLan Fong, the master, came, and she spent an hour singing opera arias with him as an accompanist on the *erh-hu*.

I served them refreshment and drinks — chrysanthemum tea with a teaspoonful of honey soothing for the throat. Soon, just by listening, I could repeat a whole aria of an opera. I sang aloud in the bathroom. Words which I didn't know I would ask Au Ma, who explained the meaning and related the story. In this way my knowledge of Chinese opera increased rapidly. Little Peacock Lien remarked that I had a good ear for music. On alternate days the lute teacher taught her to play the lute.

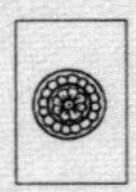

Kim says: 'We're flying down to Melbourne for a weekend, to see a modern opera called *The Phantom of the Opera*, a musical, which will not be shown in Sydney.'

An opera! And all the way to Melbourne, that city with its broad avenues and green parklands, the yellow River Yarra and cable cars. Our hotel is within walking distance of the Princess Theatre, and we stroll three blocks to Chinatown for dinner. Kim stops at a corner chemist shop to say hello to her friend Mr Lee, a fifth generation Chinese.

'He's an ABC,' she says, 'Australian-born Chinese.'

Mr Lee's aunt comes in with her shopping bag, to hand her nephew a black and white photograph of a Chinese family with their amahs taken many many years ago in Darwin, when Mr Lee was only a toddler. I recognise the attire of that period, about sixty years ago, when I was working in the House of Tang. The men in the photo have long queues, and the women have their hair knotted in chignons, and wear loose tunics and baggy pants. Mr Lee's aunt speaks with a strong Australian twang, and is wearing a dress.

'I wonder how old his aunt is?' I ask out of curiosity.

Mr Lee whispers: 'She's in her eighties.'

'She must have been here for a very long time,' I remark. She's entertaining the salesgirls in the shop who are fascinated by her animated talk.

'She's this one.' Mr Lee points to the photograph, and says: 'She's brought this for me to make copies for the

Museum of Chinese Heritage depicting the story of the early immigration of the Chinese.'

I remember a gossip session in the House of Tang when Ho Ma told us how a whole village of men had signed up as indentured labourers to go to the 'New Gold Mountain', and some young men even hurriedly got married before they left.

'This is the "New Gold Mountain" and America the old one,' Kim tells me.

Ho Ma told us that she had heard some of the indentured labourers were killed in riots that broke out on the goldfields, and many foreign labourers were massacred, but more Chinese were recruited in another shipment for, despite the risks, it was a rare opportunity to leave the poverty of China and seek fortune abroad.

Kim says: 'I'll take you on a day trip to Bendigo, where the tourists can still pan for gold and gaze at the monuments left behind by the Chinese in the gold rush. There's an old temple, now restored, which you can visit.'

'Ho Ma said many Chinese tried to steal the gold for themselves, and a few even struck it rich and returned to the village to look for Chinese wives.'

'Gold teeth is one way to smuggle gold out,' Kim suggests showing her uneven teeth.

The ascent to our seats in the theatre is as daunting as the climb of the Great Wall of China, steep steps, winding staircase, which seem never ending, and more steps and steeper ones to reach our seats which seem suspended on high.

'Good exercise for you, go to the toilet now before the show starts and try to practise self-control during the intermission, cross your legs. Ha ha!' Kim continues: 'They're the best seats up here, because you can see the whole chandelier swinging and falling from the ceiling.'

The art-deco, the balcony seats, the choreography and the make-up are impressive, but as I can't understand English and do not appreciate Western music, I soon lapse into a doze . . .

It's Friday again, and dressed in my starched white tunic and black baggy pants, I wait anxiously for our transport, straining my ears to hear the honk of a car horn, for we're driven to and fro by Mr Xi's chauffeur. Friday is our usual opera day. We have an early dinner, after which Little Peacock Lien spends a long time doing her make-up. The thoughtful Mr Xi always secures the best seats for us, purchased and reserved in advance. Little Peacock Lien sits between Au Ma and me, the seats are all hard wooden ones, not upholstered, we pad her seat and back with cushions, and take turns to fan her. The stage is brightly lit. A red satin curtain shimmers with black sequins. It is a stage opera, the Kwangdong version of the Peking Opera, sung in Cantonese. The prelude is a confusion of noise — drum rolls, cymbals and striking of gongs — so loud and deafening that it drowns any attempts at conversation. From the moment the curtain is drawn and the show starts, I sit on edge, my breath suspended, my eyes glued to the stage, dazzled by the colourful costumes glittering with sequins of gold and silver, the elaborate headgear of the heroines, their wigs and long hairpins dangling with ornaments of fake jade and pearls, the costumes of the heroes studded with many flags and pom-poms . . .

'Look at that, the chandelier's coming down,' Kim says. I look up at the huge umbrella-like lamp of dangling crystals descending rapidly to rest on the stage without shattering or crashing.

'The Phantom, huh ugly face,' Suchin sitting next to me whispers, hiding her face with her hand. I give her a Minty and nod off again after peeping at the face half black and half white . . .

I am intrigued by the heavy face painting and try to spot the character it portrays: black for honesty, white cheeks for the scoundrels, painted white noses for the villians, green for the devils and yellow for gods or good spirits. And Au Ma slowly and softly relates the synopsis of the story on stage, always a version of some classical mythology — the black and white snake, the monkey god's havoc in sea dragon kingdom — or snatches of history: battle of the three kingdoms, or tragedy of princesses and long-suffering deserted general's wife. The theme doesn't matter. It is the singing, the glamorous costumes, and the acting — those controlled movements — that capture my attention. It's like watching those characters of the storyteller in the night street of Lung Sun come alive before my eyes . . .

And suddenly there's loud clapping of hands, the actors and actresses all appear to take their bows in front of the audience, the curtain falls, and everybody stands up, putting on their coats or jackets, ready to leave. I make my way cautiously down the stairway, holding on to Suchin on one side and Kim on the other.

'How did you enjoy the show?' Kim asks.

'I'm surprised to see so many female actresses. In Chinese opera traditionally women were not permitted on stage. Men sang in falsetto voice of a female, and wore female costumes and make-up. And they excelled at it too. MeiLan Fong, the tutor of Little Peacock Lien, was such a well-known transvestite actor.'

'I can't stand the Chinese operatic singing, sounds like screeching of a cat,' Kim says.

'I used to look forward to Friday night when I was working in Hong Kong, the opera was a feast for my eyes and ears, an image I would retain until next Friday, the next opera night,' I mutter to myself.

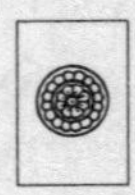

Au Ma and I jumped for joy when Mr MeiLan Fong announced that Little Peacock Lien had been selected to appear as a main star in a concert scheduled to take place in a month. Mr Xi was very pleased also, and gave Little Peacock Lien great encouragement by promising to support her with his presence every Wednesday night. The rehearsals for the concert began in earnest. I accompanied Little Peacock Lien to the theatre in a separate rickshaw, carrying all her dresses and make-up, and a thermos-flask of chrysanthemum tea with honey.

A week before the concert, Hong Kong was suddenly inundated with prints of Little Peacock Lien in yellow pamphlets — the 'street invitations'. Posters of her were glued to the walls of derelict buildings, pillars in marketplaces, lamp-posts, shopfronts. Smaller pamphlets were handed out to passers-by by shopkeepers, vendors, hawkers.

Au Ma read the four lines just below her image.

'*Little Peacock Lien. The great star with the golden voice, appearing at the Neptune Theatre, Queen St, Central. Date: eighth day of the eighth moon nightly from nine o'clock for two months.*' Also mentioned in smaller words were her co-stars Little Phoenix and Mr Yuan, the musician.

'I can't read,' I said. 'Never went to school.'

'I never went to school either,' said Au Ma. 'Most of us are self-taught. You can learn and memorise words here and there if you make an effort. If you can't read you are blind.

You should learn to read, open your eyes to see. It's easier to learn when you're young.'

'Please show me how.'

'All right. A word a day. Start with the words on this pamphlet. Copy each stroke, each line, draw them within an imaginary square. Keep practising until you know the sound and meaning of each ideogram. That's how I learned. And don't be shy to ask people. Knowledge means "learn and ask" literally, and it's not really difficult, you find clues of the meaning of the ideograms.' Then Au Ma illustrated with a drawing and writing. 'These three dots represent drops of water, so if you see this prefix in a word you can guess it's related to something liquid, like this in "sea" or "soup".'

It took me days to memorise a word. I used a black lead pencil to draw on the back of the yellow pamphlets. Au Ma was my teacher. By the time the concert opened, I could read and write most words on the pamphlet.

On her opening night we servants were given the two end seats on the front row. We had to strain our necks to look up at the stage. Crowds pushed into the hall, filling the seats. Long queues waited impatiently at the ticket box. More chairs were brought in, wedged in between rows. They too were quickly taken up. Soon there was standing room only at the back and sides. People were talking, spitting, fanning themselves. Vendors forced their way in to reach the audience, shouting: 'peanuts, sesame fritters, candies'.

Au Ma said: 'Such a concert is an informal social gathering, the songs and music are secondary, sort of a background, that's why people chat loudly, eat, drink, spit, tell jokes, argue . . .'

Kim has been given an extra ticket to the ABC Family Concert at the Sydney Opera House.

'Why don't you come along? It's a very light concert, not heavy classical music, won't send you off to dreamland, you might even enjoy it.'

I'm most impressed by the discipline observed within the concert hall. As soon as the bell rings everybody is seated, and silence prevails; latecomers even have to wait outside until the next item in the programme. No talking, drinking or eating, no addition of extra seats, a total absence of vendors. I recognise some of the tunes — nursery rhymes and songs that they play on 'Sesame Street', and that tune which Suchin scratches on her tiny violin while listening to an audio tape, 'Twinkle Twinkle Little Star', in the Suzuki method of teaching music.

A far cry from the Chinese concert at which Little Peacock Lien starred. Even after the thick maroon velvet curtains are drawn, the audience continues to talk, paying no attention to the announcement on the microphone. The first item begins when a man in a long flowing gown of navy blue silk walks to the centre of the stage, sits on a chair, supporting upright on his lap an instrument like a violin, but with only two strings. He starts sawing away with a bow, varying the tension on the two strings with his left middle and index fingers. The *erh-hu* produces the most melancholy sounds. But as he plays on, the sadness dissipates with the dexterity of his fingers and the rhythmic flow of the bow. The man's facial expression lightens. He lifts his head now and then. His face is like dry orange peel, brown, and full of pits and holes — ugly. But with his music, he guides us from the woe, the sadness, the ugliness. Beautiful sounds, sharp, short, 'Ti-di Chi-mi- Ee-ee Wu-wu . . .', pounding a melody to which one can dance, rock and sway. The audience shouts words of encouragement. His tune gathers pace, ending at a single high 'Chi . . .' He vanishes from sight. No one applauds. People start chatting loudly again, while children cry. Vendors emerge once more to peddle their wares: preserved red fruits, prawn crackers, and ice-sticks.

During the intermission Kim, Suchin and I go outside where I'm directed to the toilet, while Suchin sucks an ice-stick purchased from a counter selling soft drinks and popcorn. From the large terrace outside the glass doors we admire the coloured lights of the north shore and enjoy the refreshing breeze from the harbour. It's here that the people smoke, talk, and joke, and when the bell rings once more we enter for the second half of the programme. In complete silence again.

At the first concert of Little Peacock Lien, during the intermission, I heard the man next to me telling his neighbour: 'Little Phoenix is next, she's very good, but cannot beat Little Peacock Lien who is supreme. I've heard them in Shanghai. It's impossible to describe that particular quality, that special timbre of sound. Even the best of the sing-song girls are no match.'

Little Phoenix had a plump face, powdered white, and cheeks red with rouge, her hair swirled into two coils behind each ear. She wore a *cheongsam* of white satin and high side slits with a corsage of artificial roses in her collar.

She started on a note, and used it as a springboard from

which to take off. The musician played his *erh-hu* in a swift racy tempo, while she, with drumsticks in hand, punctuated the beat at the appropriate time. She recited verses of a poem in tune with the music; recounting fast like the galloping of horses. Yet every word was clear. The audience tapped their feet, and moved their heads with the rhythm. And when she finished, they roared with applause and encouragement. Little Phoenix shyly bowed and disappeared. And an image of the other girl who had come to the House of Tang to join the MeiLan Fong troupe returned to me, and I realised Little Phoenix had been the other messenger who reported to us the kidnap of Chiang Kai-shek in the Xian incident.

Next the spotlight focused on Little Peacock Lien, in a scarlet *cheongsam* with broad black edging. With flushed cheeks, lips of vermilion, and straight black fringe, her very presence was electrifying. Her sharp black eyes looked piercingly at the audience, from corner to corner, row to row, so that each person felt penetrated by her eyes. And as a great silence enveloped the hall she sat on a chair, while a lute page arranged the instrument on a stand close by for her.

Little Peacock Lien opened her mouth to sing, emitting a note pure as snowflake floating in the air. And gradually the note was shaped into a melody, sweet and clear, and gathered life and breath, numbing, tantalising and penetrating you, piercing your heart, steering down into the pit of your stomach so that you felt a cramp, in compassion with her voice. She broke into a familiar chorus, her dainty fingers stroking the lute with a caress that sent a million sensations into your ears. And with the musical syllables the cranes came alive fluttering their out-spread wings, and with a crescendo they soared into the azure vault of the sky.

The audience was stunned, silent, spellbound. Then deafening applause broke out, with shouts of '*cai lai, cai lai*' (encore). The audience stood up, mesmerised, with tears of appreciation in their eyes.

The concert lasted for two months. Every show was packed. Mr Xi attended every Wednesday, sat in his private box, came back to the apartment separately, stayed for supper and left without resting.

Little Peacock Lien became very famous. Her photo appeared on the front page of newspapers and magazines.

But fame shattered our once peaceful household routine. Our 'electric talkie' rang incessantly. My duty was to screen the calls for Little Peacock Lien, while she personally arranged interviews with the press, sessions with the radio and the journalists of women's magazines. We weren't allowed to reveal our address. Mr Xi would not permit it; the apartment was his 'golden house for his secret mistress', his private love-nest. So Little Peacock Lien picked a place to hold her interviews — the coffee house at the Peninsula Hotel. I was fascinated by the potted palms and high ceiling with hanging electric fans and all the waiters dressed in black Western jackets with tails and black bowties and white gloves. Little Peacock Lien had decided to change her image — an imitation of a Hollywood film star. Her long, straight black hair was trimmed and treated with chemicals, rolled and sizzled with metal clips connected to electric cords. The end result was a mass of tumbling curls. I took hours to iron her dresses with puff-sleeves and swirling skirts. And balancing herself in pointed high-heeled shoes, she would often exclaim to me: '*Aiyah*, lucky I didn't have my feet bound like your Tai Tai at the House of Tang.'

I became her shadow, following or standing behind her, clutching a basket with her make-up, flask of chrysanthemum tea and own teacup and silver chopsticks — she was afraid of catching germs from using other people's utensils.

There were endless social activities: interviews, parties, guest appearances, official opening ceremonies for Little Peacock Lien to cut ribbons. We rushed from one cocktail party to another: important sessions with the impresarios and agents who offered her contracts for concerts, plays, films.

Au Ma and I were very pleased for her, and I was very proud of her success. Whenever I met with my three sisters, our topic was Little Peacock Lien and how far and fast her fame had spread.

'She is very famous now and will earn a lot of money from the concerts and stage shows,' Ah Han said.

'In which case she won't have to depend entirely on Mr Xi for money.'

'Most women depend on men for their livelihood.'

'But Mr Xi treats her like a plaything, like keeping a pet, for his pleasure only. She is dressed and made-up in the way he likes, and not allowed to have her friends, not even Little Phoenix, in her flat. She has to arrange an alternative place for her press interviews and to entertain her fellow-singers,' I told them.

We sisters met regularly, on the first day and the fifteenth of each month, and we would spend the day at the nunnery praying to Kuan Yin and eating in their vegetarian restaurant, while catching up with all the gossip and news. We met other groups of sisterhood at the nunnery, and had made a few friends who also worked as domestics. And we would compare notes about the current rate of salary and the bonuses we were paid, and how we were treated, and were given introductions for jobs. One particular group of sisters, Ah Chun, Kam, Eng and Goh, had become very good friends, and we even pooled together to rent an apartment where we could go if we were sick or when we needed somewhere to spend a few days in between jobs. It was also a place to store our personal things.

Finally Little Peacock Lien accepted an offer to play the main role in an 'electric shadow.' To star in a film.

'It's been my dream since I was a child to become a movie star!' Little Peacock Lien said. 'At last my wish has come true. My ambition is realised.'

She showed Au Ma and me her scrapbook of cuttings from newspapers and magazines. It was filled with pictures of American movie stars.

'This is Shirley Temple, look at her head of curls, so young, yet already starred in a few movies. I saw this one called *Poor Little Rich Girl*.' And she turned a page. 'Bette Davis, she got an award, the coveted Oscar for the movie *Jezebel*.' We saw a flyer of a cartoon by Walt Disney, *Snow White and the Seven Dwarfs*. 'It's still showing in the Queen's cinema, you must go to see it on your day off, Ah Silver,' she said. 'I know Au Ma gets a headache from the cinema, she can't stand sitting in the dark and watching electric shadow.'

As part of the film contract, Little Peacock Lien was given the use of a chauffeured limousine, transport for attending an intensive acting course at the movie studio. I watched her learn to vocalise, to gesticulate, to walk, express emotions, to sing, to dance . . .

Mr Xi was annoyed by her absence during his Wednesday visits. He became impatient, he threw tantrums, lost his temper, and when she returned a big quarrel ensued, for since Little Peacock Lien had become famous, she hardly had time for Mr Xi. I could feel the tension in the air. Both Little Peacock Lien and Mr Xi were agitated, tempers flared easily. Heated arguments and harsh words replaced the laughter, songs, and music of the old days.

Then the shooting began. The hours were irregular. Sometimes we stayed in the studio till late at night. Depending on the locations we were exposed to sun, rain and wind. I helped Little Peacock Lien with her make-up and dressing. The shooting was often interrupted or repeated until the director was satisfied and she found the work strenuous and exhausting under intense bright lights. Mr Xi found out that there was a male actor involved in some intimate scenes and he objected strongly.

'He's jealous,' Au Ma explained. 'But there is nothing he can do as it is part of the contract to star opposite this male actor.'

Little Peacock Lien was now earning a large income, and became less dependent financially on Mr Xi.

One day a youth with dark sunglasses handed her a note.

'*Aiyah*, I have to pay protection money, two dollars per month.'

'Two dollars of the old king's money? That's one fifth of my salary per month!' I said. The British king, George V, had died just a couple of months before and it was rumoured that his money would be worth a lot more in a few years time, as no more of his notes would be printed. 'Why don't you consult Mr Xi regarding this matter?' I asked.

'No, he won't help, I know, he'll say I'm responsible for my own doings. He won't dare to be involved, in case his identity is revealed and his wife finds out about the whole thing.'

Au Ma said she would talk to her husband about this on her next day off, as he would know what to advise.

'My old man says you'll have to pay up the protection money, and let it be known which group you're paying to, so that other groups won't come and bother you,' she told Little Peacock Lien after speaking to her husband.

I thought about this on the way to the market. 'What will happen if she won't pay, or can't afford to pay?' I asked Au Ma.

'*Aiyah*, they've done their homework, they know how much her income is before they approach her, and they ask a percentage of her gross. If she refuses to pay they'll harm her, ruin her reputation, or release snakes in the concert hall to scare the audience away or start a fire . . . as they've done in the past to other artists. Remember Butterfly Wing, the actress who refused to pay protection money? They frightened her so much that she became a nervous wreck.' Au Ma sighed, shaking her head. 'It's a status symbol, to pay protection money, a sign of success, according to my husband.'

So Little Peacock Lien wrote a note to the young man with the dark glasses when he approached her the next time.

I was responsible for delivering a red-packet to a young man, dressed in traditional tunic and long pants, identified as Number 432, once a month in a busy market lane.

'May I know what organisation we're contributing to?' I asked him. He rolled up his sleeve to show me a tattoo on his arm: a triangle, formed by three dots and joined by three lines. 'The three sided group?' He simply ignored me and walked away, merging with the crowd.

The storyteller in Lung Sun used to entertain us with stories of the martial arts experts of Shaolin Monastery, in the Hunan province, the holy fathers of Kung Fu. In the epic of the Fire of Shaolin Temple, one hundred and ten out of one hundred and eighteen monks perished in the fire, betrayed by a monk called Ma Ling Yee. Of the eight who fled, only five survived, and they managed to cross a river by means of a straw sandal which turned into a boat in time to save them. They became the first Ancestors of the Triad Societies, who set up Lodges all over China.

'They're called the Black Society or the Tongs, there are many groups of Triads with different names and leaders,' Au Ma said. 'Huh, they're always mentioned in the news for their involvement in criminal activities like drug-trafficking, gambling rackets, prostitution, extortion from kidnappings, demands for protection money . . . And the police force is infiltrated or bribed by them.'

'But they had such noble ideals when they first started out, trying to rid the Mongolian conquerors from the Chinese throne.'

'Now they have no hesitation in killing and maiming, it's best not to antagonise them.'

'It was common practice when I was in Shanghai,' Little Peacock Lien said. 'The Black Society demand money from even the street hawkers and beggars, in the name of protection. I suppose we Chinese have become so accustomed to having to pay off someone through the centuries — imperial officials, the police, the tax collectors — that now we feel quite helpless to protest.'

The day the shooting was finally completed we returned to find Mr Xi in the apartment, pacing the floor, waiting for Little Peacock Lien. He was in a good mood, and I served him his favourite tea, as usual. Then he led Little Peacock Lien into her room, and I could hear them talking in low voices.

Hong Kong had been rocked by the statement issued by Prince Edward, the would-be successor to the English throne, in defence of his abdication. For the love of a woman. An American divorcee. It spurred many clandestine lovers to come out into the open, this public confession of love, a heroic romance. And Mr Xi too, under this influence, had gathered courage to forsake his 'throne'.

The following morning Little Peacock Lien wrote down the date and time, month and year of her birth. Since each date is represented by two characters, this is referred to as the eight characters of her horoscope. She sent for Au Ma and me.

'Au Ma, take my eight characters to request a *chim* from the soothsayer.'

'With regards to what?'

'Marriage.'

'A marriage to whom?'

'Mr Xi.'

'*Aiyah*, but he's already married . . .'

'Last night he proposed to me. He's prepared to leave his wife.'

'We'll need his eight characters too,' Au Ma reminded her.

'He was born on the fifteenth day of the third moon, thirty years older than myself. I don't know the time of his birth. Take Ah Silver with you, good experience for her, to learn of this aspect of custom and culture in Chinese life in Hong Kong.'

The Temple of Wong Tai Sin was a fascinating place. Beggars crowded at its entrance. Two concentric clusters of stalls surrounded the courtyard leading to the Temple, the outer selling paper money, joss-sticks, candles, oil for lamps, pictures of deities, charms and worry beads. The inner circle was occupied by the stalls of palmists, fortune-tellers, soothsayers.

Au Ma made offerings of fruits, paper ingots and incense, and obtained a bamboo cannister of *chims* or bamboo tapers, each with a number on it. We knelt in the courtyard, and prayed to Wong Tai Sin to help solve Little Peacock Lien's problem. Au Ma then agitated the cannister with cupped hands. One bamboo taper dropped out. We noted the number, and took it to one of the soothsayers. We chose one with an honest face.

'*Sinseh*, how much to read a *chim*?'

'Eighty cents.'

'Too expensive. Fifty cents.'

'All right, you are my first customers. Sit down, you have a bargain.'

He noted the number of the taper, asked its purpose, checked each horoscope. He consulted two books. 'It's a bad *chim* for her,' he said eventually.

Au Ma and I gasped in disbelief.

'Look for yourself. It's a low *chim*.' He showed us his book. '*Chims* are divided into high — good, middle, so so; and low — bad.'

He opened another book, and read a poem of eight word stanzas.

'With open arms and heart she greets him
Though prospects of marriage seem far and grim
Already betrothed to a princess, pledged to marry
His position is general-commander of an army
Bestowed by her father, King of the land
My sweet, my love, please try and understand
Concentrate on your sing-song, drown your
sorrow
In your music, the lyrics, forget about tomorrow.
When war is over, victorious I will return

Not to your arms, no longer your concern.'

'It's the legend of the famous general in the Sung dynasty who fell in love with a beautiful sing-song girl, but couldn't marry her because he was betrothed to a princess before he left for the war,' he explained. 'In her life she's not destined to be legally married, only a lover or mistress. If she forces the issue then the harmony will be upset.'

We boarded a bus home, disheartened.

Au Ma related the soothsayer's advice word for word to Little Peacock Lien.

'I admit he's married, but he doesn't love his wife; last night he said he is prepared to divorce her to marry me,' Little Peacock Lien said. Despite the bad *chim*, she still had faith in Mr Xi.

The electric shadow opened to a full house daily. Little Peacock Lien became even more famous. Her name was displayed in lights outside the movie houses, and a large poster of her stretched across the awning at the entrance. She became very rich from the royalties, and her protection money was increased by a dollar per month. She signed another contract and stayed up late at night for weeks learning the script. Then the shooting began.

One morning the door to her dressing-room in the movie studio was suddenly thrown open. In charged two women, chests heaving and breath puffing. The stout one dashed to the dressing-table with the three panelled mirrors, banged its glass top and shouted: 'Where is the vile fox, the witch? Come out of your hiding place.'

With one motion she swept the table clean of its contents; combs, make-up jars, headgear, ribbons and jewellery fell to the floor with a crash.

I was busy helping Little Peacock Lien change her dress behind the screen. I poked my head out. 'Are you out of your mind? Get out of here, you're wrecking the place. I'll call the guard,' I shouted, while Little Peacock Lien was struggling to get her costume over her head.

The second woman now spoke: '*Aiyah*, don't hurt yourself, Rose, let's go. You're lowering your status by coming to such a place.' She tried to drag Rose away.

Rose pushed her aside. 'Come out, you stinker.' She shook her fist; a wet patch of sweat showed through her yellow *cheongsam*. Her eyes shone with hatred. Her hairpin fell out of her chignon as she trembled with rage.

The second lady repeated: 'Don't lower yourself, Rose, let's get out of here.'

'I must have it out with her once and for all,' Rose shouted.

Little Peacock Lien made a rustling noise as she finally tugged her costume on.

Rose rushed towards the screen, pushing me aside. I fell against the wall. She snatched Little Peacock Lien's collar. With the other hand she slapped her face. 'Leave my husband alone,' she yelled, stamping her feet.

Little Peacock Lien cried *Aiyah*, with pain, her hand raised to her cheek. Then, on impulse, she charged at Rose, pulling her hair. Both women were now locked in combat, clawing at each other's faces and pulling hair, tearing dresses.

I got up and ran outside to the corridor, shouting for help.

By this time a small crowd of onlookers, chorus girls and supporting actresses had gathered outside our door. Rose was pulled aside by her friend who stood between the two fighters, separating them. Rose's collar was torn, a large jade pendant on a thick gold choker dangled out.

I dragged Little Peacock Lien to one side.

'Just wait and see, husband snatcher,' Rose shrieked. She hopped away on one shoe, her friend tugging her along.

I quickly bolted the door.

Little Peacock Lien sat down and cried, her heavy make-up smudged by the tears. I picked up the things from the floor, and fetched a basin of warm water and a towel to clean the make-up from her face.

I thought to myself: the fortune-teller was right. Amazing that he could tell the future with such accuracy for fifty cents.

Mr Xi came to our apartment furtively on two more occasions. He broke down and apologised to Little Peacock Lien, explaining that he was not in a position to divorce his wife yet as he was only an employee in her father's firm. Later, he promised, when he had established his own business, he would divorce Rose and marry her . . .

He left some money in an envelope.

The day after Mr Xi's visit, Little Peacock Lien left as usual for the studio. Just as she was about to enter the limousine someone called her name. She turned around and looked up. Something hit her face. She winced. '*Aiyah!*' she cried. It was an acid bomb. Her loud cries of agony echoed through the street. It all happened so quickly that I didn't know how to react. But after a few seconds I recovered, and helped her into the car. Luckily her eyes had been shut at that crucial second, as she held her hands up to shield them. The hands were very red. The chauffeur drove to the nearest doctor who summoned an ambulance to rush her to hospital. On her hands and face large red blisters appeared. She complained of great throbbing pain. Frequent injections were needed to calm her.

Mr Xi never went to see her at all in the hospital. He came to the apartment with his chauffeur, and a suitcase to collect all his things, including some pieces of furniture, and the antique looking glass. Then he could not be contacted. His office staff said he had left on a business trip overseas, with no forwarding address, and the date of his return uncertain.

Little Peacock Lien was forced to terminate her contract. She was told that her face and hands would be scarred and disfigured for life. She would not be able to appear in movies any more.

The youth identified as Number 432 visited Little Peacock Lien at the hospital.

'I'm sent by Big Brother, who is not able to come personally. He sends his concern and regards and thanks you for your past patronage.'

'Who is Big Brother?'

'The "cumshaw".'

'What's "cumshaw"?'

'Protection money, steak money, kickback.'

'Extortion money. The Triad!'

'Call it what you like. It's a way of life.'

'Thank your Big Brother for his kindness.'

'He wants to help you. Tell us about your enemies or suspects.'

Little Peacock Lien's voice began to falter. 'I have no

enemy. Please don't cause any more trouble.' She started to sob. 'Leave me alone,' she shrieked.

The nurse was summoned to sedate her and I showed the youth the way out.

'Please leave my mistress alone. She has enough suffering. Don't bother her any more please . . .'

Au Ma told me that she suspected we were being followed. We took care to vary our visiting time each day. One day Number 432 confronted me at the entrance to the hospital.

'Don't run away, Silver Sister. Your relative is here to see you.'

'Ah Sai!'

I couldn't believe my eyes. There before me was my brother Ah Sai, whom I had left behind at the wharf in Canton with Uncle Fatty Lee. My impulse was to reach for him, hug him tight, my little brother, that toddler with the snot running down his nose, but he stood tall, aloof, and arrogant. I clasped his hands, and felt his well-trimmed nails. He seemed embarrassed and disentangled himself from my hold, clearing his throat while tears dripped from my eyes.

'Come into the coffee shop where you can sit down and talk.' No. 432 guided us all to a table.

'You have not changed much in three years, sister Ah Pah, except that your pigtail has grown in length.' His voice had changed. It was now deep and sonorous, that of an adult male.

Ah Sai leaned forward in his chair, tracing my pigtail with his eyes. 'It must reach down to your hip, eh? Still a black and white, I see, and how are the "sisters?"' There was a hint of sarcasm in his tone. It was of course my trademark as a 'comb-up' to wear my long hair in plait, baggy black pants, and immaculately starched white tops.

Number 432 cleared his throat, a sign to Ah Sai to get

on with business. Ah Sai quickly changed the subject.

'I have something very important to ask you,' he said, taking a sepia photograph from his wallet. 'Can you identify these two persons?'

The figures, though blurred, were familiar. How could I forget Rose after the brawl in the dressing room.

'It's Rose and Mr Xi,' I said. 'Where did you find this photo?'

He ignored my question, and showed it to Au Ma, who said after scrutinising it: 'This is Mr Xi, but I have never seen the lady.'

Ah Sai looked at Number 432, who nodded, satisfied with the result of identification. He snatched the photo and left.

'What does he plan to do?' I asked Ah Sai.

'Nothing harmful to anyone.' And he snapped his fingers to attract the waiter's attention. 'Three cups of coffee please.'

'How did you get involved with No 432?'

'What do you mean involved? I'm a member of the Honorable Society,' he exclaimed with pride.

'A member of the Triad? You don't mean it!' I looked at him, shocked.

'Don't be alarmed, Ah Pah, or should I call you Silver Sister? I'm not a criminal. I belong to my fraternity like you belong to your sorority of amahs.'

'But the Triads have gang fights and clashes with police. They extort money, smuggle drugs, kill. Leave your Society. I can get you a good job in the Taipan of Taikoo Hung. Please,' I implored Ah Sai. 'Why can't you do a decent trade as a cabinet maker?'

'That cabinet maker in Canton ran away like you. I had to survive.' He told me how Uncle Fatty Lee had died of some disease and that he'd had to bury him with his bare hands. 'I was in the street begging, thieving, starving, in rags. When Chiang Kai-shek retreated to Canton two years ago he declared war on the Japanese, who took city after city in the north, Peiping, Shanghai . . . Refugees flooded Canton by the thousands. You left just in time. The Japanese were ruthless animals, I heard about their many atrocities when they took Nanking . . .'

He tapped the ashes of his cigarette into a spittoon under the table, and crossed his legs revealing expensive imported leather shoes.

'Where would I be if the Triads hadn't recruited me? Dead and dumped in the Pearl River, that's where.' He rolled down the sleeve of his jacket, covering the tattoo of three dots arranged in a triangle that I had already seen on the arm of Number 432.

'Membership is for life, sister,' he went on. 'I can't quit. I've been sworn to thirty-six oaths, learned every word by heart. If I should die in the course of my duty, you will be provided for. Your name is in my dossier as next of kin.'

With a shudder I shouted: 'I don't want any of your dirty money. You can keep all the cash for yourself.'

'Calm down, Ah Pah.'

He beckoned to the waiter for the bill, and started to describe the elaborate ceremony of initiation he had undergone in Canton.

'Enough, enough. I don't want to hear any more of such barbaric ritual,' I told him.

I stood up to go, Au Ma following me.

'I expect to meet you same time next month,' Ah Sai said. 'After all, I'm the only blood relative you have left — your only brother. This is my electric talkie number. Ask for Straw Sandal, that's me.'

That night I tossed and turned, haunted by dreams of

elaborate ceremonies in grotesque temples; of Ah Sai beheading cockerels, drinking wine laced with ashes, bleeding fingers to mix blood with other members, trampling over firepits, supervised by the chief — The White Fan — swearing his thirty-six oaths. I woke up screaming, scorched with fever, bathed in sweat. Terrified.

I tried to put my fears for Ah Sai out of my mind. Hong Kong was busy preparing for the coronation of the new English king, George VI. Decorations, flags, red banners with congratulatory messages were flying in every street. A procession was planned with floats from many big Hongs and companies of Hong Kong. On the night of the twelfth of May, 1937, firecrackers exploded non-stop, and the sky was filled with most unusual and elaborate fireworks. My sisters and I stood on the vantage point of Victoria Peak to watch.

But Au Ma wasn't interested in these events. She had her own problems. She confided to me that her husband Au Lao was in hiding from his creditors for gambling debts. Au Ma couldn't ask for an advance of her pay as Little Peacock Lien was in hospital, with no income. I took her few pieces of jewellery to the local pawnshop for valuation, as she was too embarrassed to do it herself. But it was not the price she had hoped to get.

One night soon after that I was woken by a tap-tap sound. It seemed to be coming from the back door.

'Who can it be at this time in the night?' Au Ma whispered.

We tiptoed to the air-well and leaned over to peep at the landing of the fire staircase. A dark figure moved, moaned in pain.

'It's me, Au Lao . . .'

'*Aiyah*, it's your husband, let him in quick, go get the key.'

Au Ma did as she was told, in a daze. I unlocked the padlock and Au Lao fell in as soon as the door was opened.

He lay on the floor, bleeding from the forehead. We lifted him into the kitchen, laid him on a mat, and Au Ma cleaned his wounds with a hot towel. His face was swollen, the right eye black and blue, and his arms were covered in scratches.

'He needs medical attention,' I said to Au Ma. 'I'll get a doctor on the electric talkie.'

'No, no,' he protested. 'This will alert the police and I'll be in more trouble. The Big EarLobes are after me — my gambling debts . . . As it is they'll track me down, I've missed the deadline for payment. They've threatened to beat me until the debt is paid up.'

Au Ma and I racked our brains to think of a safe hiding place if a search party should come to the apartment. We looked here and there, at cupboards and under shelves and beds, and finally agreed on an ideal spot.

The next day there was an urgent knock on the front door, followed by an impatient kick. We hid Au Lau in the air-well as we had rehearsed; he clung to the trellis floor of slatted wood, covered by the cantilevered bamboo poles of clothes.

Four men pushed open the door, and rushed past us looking everywhere, up turning urns and trunks.

'Where's he hiding? We demand payment.'

'Here,' Au Ma came out with her box of meagre gold jewellery. 'Please accept as part payment.'

One of them rummaged through the assortment in the box and laughed. 'Ha, that's not worth anything.'

Before they left, the one with a scar on his right cheek

said: 'We'll be back in two days, be ready with the cash. He owes us four thousand dollars. Remember, cash or else . . . '

'Four thousand dollars! I thought he only borrowed one thousand.'

'It's principal and interest, and the interest accrues daily, compounded,' Au Lao explained as he emerged from the air-well.

Au Ma sat down and cried: '*Aiyah*, where am I going to raise four thousand dollars? They'll kill you.' And she bawled in hysterics, she who was always so calm and serious, now lost her head.

'They want his money, not his life,' I reminded her. 'A dead person cannot pay, they won't kill him, it's only a threat. I'll discuss with Ah Sai and his gang, maybe their Big Brother can help. Remeber they offered to help Little Peacock Lien not so long ago . . .'

'Should we talk to Little Peacock Lien first?' Au Ma asked me.

'No, she has enough problems of her own, let's not bother her with your worries, I'll ask my brother instead.'

I rang Ah Sai's electric talkie number, and asked for Straw Sandal. We arranged to meet at a noodle shop in a crowded bazaar. He listened carefully as I explained Au Lao's predicament.

'I'll discuss with my superiors. Debts must be paid, with interest.'

'But not at such an inflated rate.'

'That is the way the Big EarLobes work. Let this be a lesson to him, never gamble with borrowed money, never have anything to do with the Big EarLobes in future.'

At our next meeting Ah Sai assured me that Big Brother had been informed, and negotiations were taking place. A week later, a figure had been reached, a sum equivalent to the principal plus the current bank rate of interest, one thousand and two hundred dollars, to be paid within sixty days.

Au Ma cried: '*Aiyah*, where am I going to get the rest of the money, my jewellery is only worth a hundred and fifty dollars.'

'Be patient,' I urged her. 'Remember the old saying "Heavens will not point a no-through road to men". There must be a way out — let's find out from the Wong Tai Sin Temple *chim*.'

'It is now a tourist attraction,' Kim says after her visit to Hong Kong. 'Your favourite place for predictions into the future, the Temple of Wong Tai Sin. Countless coaches take the Japanese and Chinese from mainland China and Taiwan to visit there every day, hundreds of gamblers adjust their bets according to the Wong Tai Sin's *chims*.'

'If they're too commercialised, the predictions churned out automatically by computers for the tourist trade, then they can't be accurate any more, they're for fun, and shouldn't be taken seriously.'

'Costs ten dollars per *chim* nowadays. Does one have to pray and make offerings and burn incense in order to attain accuracy?'

'Not only that, you have to believe in it. To have faith, like in any religion.'

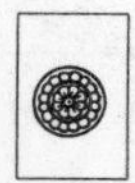

'Fifty cents please, this time for myself,' Au Ma said to the same soothsayer, the one with the honest face, after she had prayed and made her offerings of fruits, paper ingots and burned her joss-sticks.

'I'm in deep trouble, financial problem.'

The soothsayer nodded, while he looked up his book for the number of the *chim*.

'It's a very high *chim*, excellent.' Then he delved into his second book of poems in eight word stanzas:

> 'In your darkest of day, the loneliest night
> In hour of despair, with thoughts of flight
> When poor and forsaken, cold, hungry and alone
> Help comes to you, coal glowing in snow.'

Then he explained. 'To the cold and hungry Mandarin stranded in the snow, someone who brings him the very thing he needs most: coal as fuel for cooking and warmth in the cold, is most appreciated.'

Au Ma was still dubious.

'Believe him, trust his words, he's been very accurate when he interpreted Little Peacock Lien *chim* for marriage,' I reminded her.

A week later Au Ma returned home with newspapers.

'Look, it's headlines in all newspapers: BABY XI KIDNAPPED.'

I saw a large photograph of a toddler with well-groomed hair and dimples.

Au Ma read: 'Three years old, answered to the name of Kenny, wearing a navy blue suit and English Clarke shoes of brown leather and white cotton socks with his surname

XI embroidered in red. Around his neck he wears a gold chain with a gold locket inside which is a *foo* or amulet. Master Xi disappeared from his pram in his private garden while his amah went indoors to fetch his milk bottle. Missing since the seventh day of the eighth moon.'

I recognised Rose's voice on the radio, that same squeak choked with emotions I had heard the day she went to slap Little Peacock Lien. Now she was pleading for the safe return of her son — and with promise of a very generous reward. Even any lead or information of his whereabouts would be rewarded with a thousand dollars.

When I went to visit Little Peacock Lien two plain-clothed policemen also gained access to interview her.

'Have you approached anyone for revenge or retaliation?' they asked.

'Leave me alone, isn't it enough for me to suffer with my disfigured face, and my career ruined?' Little Peacock Lien wailed, threatening suicide. She was placed under police surveillance thereafter. Even our movements were trailed. Au Ma though it was the Big EarLobes seeking news of Au Lao.

The streets of Hong Kong were becoming even more congested, swollen with more and more strangers, people from the north of China, speaking the northern dialect, like the refugees that had passed through the main mud street of Lung Sun so many years before; all burdened with baggage, backpacks, children and toddlers. They came to our local marketplaces and bazaars buying food, and talking with the locals.

'The Japanese have taken many cities in the north . . . Shanghai had a big disaster — the Chinese tried to raid the Japanese warship *Izumo*, but their aim was wrong and bombs fell on a very congested part near the International Zone where lots of refugees had fled for safety. Now even the French and the British are preparing to leave Shanghai urgently, the Japanese retaliated the following day . . .'

But we locals were too engrossed in the development of the ransom case. From the bazaar, we heard gossip that a ransom note — '*No police or else a dead baby* . . .' — had been delivered to the Xi family, with the *foo* that the toddler had been wearing.

At my next meeting with my sisters and our friends, all we could talk about was the young toddler Xi.

'It's the work of the Black Society.'

'You mean the Triad? The Tongs.'

'Who else would carry out such blackmail and extortion?'

Two days later Ah Chun had confidential news from her friend who worked in the Xi family.

'Baby Xi has been mysteriously returned to the Xi garden in the night. Safe and unscarred.'

Au Ma scanned the papers daily for news, but was disappointed, nothing ever was mentioned again. An anticlimax.

'It's all a cover-up. I suspect a large ransom money had been paid off without police interference. The case is hushed up by the press as well,' Au Ma concluded.

The police watch over Little Peacock Lien at the hospital ward was called off. Ah Sai suddenly appeared at the ward with a letter marked 'Private and Confidential' for Little Peacock Lien and he slipped off quietly without speaking to me. She read it over and over again. For the first time since her admission three months before, she smiled, looked relieved, and happy.

Quietly she told Au Ma and me: 'An insurance company has paid me a very large sum of money for the accident to my face, and they have even remitted the money into a Swiss account opened in my name. Here, Ah Silver, mail this for me, it's my acknowledgement letter, maybe it was Mr Xi who took out the insurance for me.'

A month later she came home, and discovered that Mr Xi had taken away all the gold and diamond jewellery he had bought her, including some cash of her own stored in the safe deposit box, while she had been in hospital. Perhaps to give them to his wife as a peace-offering, or to present them to his new black-market mistress. This we would never know.

'I never liked him, it's his eyes, lizard-like, he's a coward, a small man with a little heart,' I said.

'A thief,' Au Ma pronounced.

So it couldn't have been Mr Xi who arranged for the insurance pay-out, and Little Peacock Lien didn't remember taking out any insurance for herself. No matter. Money was the crucial thing, especially now she was without an income.

'It's a lot of money,' she said. 'I couldn't have earned that in my lifetime.'

So Au Ma was able to approach Little Peacock Lien for a loan to pay off her husband's debts to the Big EarLobes.

Ah Sai sent me a message on the electric talkie: he had a letter for my mistress, would I meet him at the busy noodle place at my next meeting with the three sisters, as he would like to meet them too. It was a reunion for the five of us. My three sisters told Ah Sai what a tall and handsome lad he had become, and that he must be an expert in carpentry by now. On that note Ah Sai changed the subject. He described to Ah Han how Uncle Fatty Lee had looked before he died, his complexion was deep yellow, a disease of epidemic proportion at that time.

Ah Han said: 'I sent many letters and messages to your

place of work for Uncle Fatty Lee, but got not reply.'

'My boss also migrated to Hong Kong, and Uncle Fatty Lee's quarters by the wall of the mansion were dismantled by the owners. We drifted away from place to place . . .'

'I hear that the Chinese are losing the war,' Ah Fong said. 'Chiang Kai-shek has retreated to Chung King, the Communists led by Mao have gone underground. The Japanese have taken another city, HanKow, and later the war will spread south to Hong Kong.'

'The Taikoo Hong family is planning to move from Hong Kong before the Japanese come,' Ah Yin said.

'Where is a safe place to go?' I asked

'Our friends Ah Chun, Kam, Goh and Eng are planning to go to Malaya and Singapore, also ruled by the British, but they say it's much safer there, because of the distance from China.'

'I'm staying here in Hong Kong, to be among our own Chinese people,' said Ah Sai. 'We can keep in touch if you direct your mail to this address, it's a block of apartments.' Neither Ah Sai or I wanted our sisters to know that he was a member of the Triad. It was not an identity that one liked to reveal.

I took the letter home to Little Peacock Lien

'It's from Big Brother,' she said. 'Just one line to wish me well, and recommend me to have plastic surgery to my face in America.'

'What a far-fetched idea,' Au Ma said.

'Not so, my school-friend who has gone to America to study has written, she'll be coming back for the New Year, and she too suggested facial plastic surgery for me in America. It might give me a new lease in life, now that I have the money for it.'

Little Peacock Lien wrote to her girlfriend Alice in California, asking her to recommend a good plastic surgeon for her. Alice replied that she knew of an excellent one, a specialist in remodelling Hollywood stars.

Little Peacock Lien had hardly left the apartment since she came home. Her face was badly scarred, like a crumpled, wrinkled piece of dough, her mouth stretched crooked and pulled into a cynical smile by her injuries, but her eyes were still black and piercing as before, full of life and fire. The letters from the invisible Big Brother and Alice filled her with hope and aspirations once more.

'I'm only twenty-one, and I'm rich, and if plastic surgery can really change my looks, I can lead a normal life and resume my singing and music career again.'

In the meantime she remained a recluse. Au Ma helped her to shampoo her hair, which had grown long and straight, and she wore it in a plain pigtail. There were no more visits to the hairdresser, or the opera.

I tell Kim: 'The two drawbacks of Hong Kong while I live there were water rationing and the typhoons.'

'*Aiyah*, the typhoons are still a terrible threat there, but they've solved the water problem. They've a contract with China which supplies all the water Hong Kong needs, and water is available all day and night.'

'Huh, in the old days, was a very precious commodity. We had to store water in urns, buckets, basins, when it was released for two hours in the morning and two hours in the evening.'

'My plane was diverted to Taiwan during the typhoon, and I arrived one day late for my conference.'

Here in Australia, although annual occurrences of natural disasters such as floods and bushfires are common, people are usually forewarned, and loss of lives is kept to a minimal. There is compensation from insurance companies. Since I've been in this country I've only heard of one really bad disaster: Cyclone Tracy, on Christmas day 1974. I watched this historical event on Kim's black and white television. In Sydney, as families gathered around for their Christmas dinners, with their Christmas trees in lights, and their presents in stockings, the people of Darwin were threatened by the Big Wind.

'Look,' Kim said. 'The Giant who granted your residency has cut short his European tour to return home to inspect the disaster area.'

The following month Kim's friends from Darwin, the Low Family, came to stay with us in Sydney with their two young children while Darwin was being rebuilt. Kim asked Mrs Low what had she saved, as the roof of her house was being blown away. She replied: 'I rescued the family albums. Those photographs taken and collected over so many years could never be replaced.'

I often wonder what would I rush back risking my life to save in a similar situation. Certainly not photographs. In fact, I wouldn't risk my life for anything. Life hasn't been easy for me, and nothing is more important, not money, not memorabilia.

From then on, every Christmas Day the radio and the TV reminds us how many years have passed since that disaster, and I am reminded of the typhoon that killed Au Lao

typified by a Chinese saying: 'Men can experience unexpected misfortune, Nature can suddenly churn up fast wind and waves'.

Nature turned nasty overnight, without warning came the big wind — *tai fong*— or typhoon, each gale stronger than the one before. Au Ma and I ran about the apartment, shutting all windows, the wooden louvres with shutters, and hooking them securely. But no sooner did we shut one, than another would be blown open again. We pasted sheets of old newspapers to mirrors and glass windows and partitions, and turned off the electricity mains. The wind blew with the madness of a tempest, at one hundred and fifty miles per hour. A torrential downpour came next, gushing through open windows, drenching the floor.

For two days we stayed indoors, mopping the puddles, sweeping up pieces of glass. Little Peacock Lien hid in her room, afraid of any further damage to her face from the flying glass debris. But Au Ma couldn't help worrying about her husband Au Lao, alone in the squatter town by the hill of Kowloon. Communication was impossible. The electric talkie line was dead, newspapers not delivered, and we couldn't receive any news from the radio as the electricity was turned off. By day three the rain had dwindled to a drizzle, with an occasional gust of wind. Pedestrians appeared on the road again. We heard rumours of landslides in the hills of Kowloon, with casualties and deaths. Au Ma was too terrified to check out things by herself. I offered to accompany her. There was no public transport.

We walked through a landscape of destruction and ruin: smashed windows, broken doors, torn roofs. Trees were uprooted as if by a giant hand, their gnarled trunks and branches snapped and piled across our path. Pleasure yachts and fishing boats had been overturned on the beach or wrecked against the rocks.

Au Ma's worst fear was realised.

The shanty town on the hill had collapsed and was covered by rubble. It has been declared a 'disaster area', cordoned off by the rescue team and police, while volunteer workers were digging and removing those injured.

The big wind passed, taking Au Lao's life with it. Au Ma was shocked by the gruesome death of her husband, now buried together with their home under the rocks and mud without a trace. But at least he had died debt-free, and would rest in peace wherever he might be.

That month we sisters said farewell to our friends Ah Chun, Goh, Eng and Kam, who were departing for Malaya and Singapore. We had arranged to meet them there in another month or two.

Little Peacock Lien was making preparations to leave for America with her friend Alice.

'I may take this chance to migrate there for good, and before I leave I have a little appreciation for you, for being so good to me when I needed your support most,' she said.

I received from Little Peacock Lien the sum of three thousand dollars of the old king's dollars — in 1938, this was a very substantial sum indeed.

'The Kuomintang are retreating to Formosa, passing through Hong Kong. Many more refugees are pouring into Hong Kong. It's reported that at least twelve thousand people are sleeping on the streets each night,' Ah Sai said at our last meeting in the noodle shop. 'I have to go to the border of Kowloon for another assignment, I'll say goodbye now.'

Once again I was filled with sadness, and once again Ah Sai seemed without emotion, as men don't shed tears but blood. I gave him Ah Chun's address so that he could contact me in Singapore.

Little Peacock Lien had persuaded Au Ma to go with her to America. But before they left, the apartment was sold by the Xi family and Au Ma and Little Peacock Lien moved in with Alice at her parents' home, Euston. I went with them to help carry the suitcases. It was a very impressive place behind Bonham Road. Au Ma would never need to fear the big wind here. Euston was a mock Gothic castle complete with turrets and gargoyles, with majestic granite columns and white pimlicos, surrounded by a moat of sandstone. My parting with Little Peacock Lien and Au Ma was a happy one. Little Peacock Lien was full of hope and expectation for a new 'face' and new life in a new country. And she would have Au Ma to take care of her. They would find good company in San Francisco, as Alice said: 'There is a huge Chinatown there, and I know Au Ma will haggle from stall to stall, buying the freshest of meat to cook for Little Peacock Lien. Now that Au Lao is dead she will devote all her time and attention to her mistress.'

We all promised to keep in touch, and Alice gave me an address.

I moved into the apartment with my three sisters while we waited for the next ship to sail for Singapore. By now I had a large sum of money saved, having worked for thirteen years — ten in the House of Tang, and three years with Little Peacock Lien — with free accommodation, food and clothing. For the first time in my life I went out shopping for myself: shoes, Swiss voile for my tunic tops, Thai silk for my baggy pants, a plain gold ring, and a gold chain, and a Swiss watch. My sisters were advised not to deposit any money in the bank, not safe in such volatile political climate, they were told. I slept with my vest on, the one with secret inner pockets filled with cash, and I wore my new gold chain round my neck strung with my ring, earrings, and the perfect pebble from the stream in Lung Sun. That night I fell asleep lulled by the tick-tick of my Omega watch.

Singapore

'FIFTY YEARS AGO on this day the Japanese invaded and occupied Singapore; the British troops who surrendered became prisoners of war of the famous (or infamous) Changi prison . . .' the TV commentator announces, before transmitting a documentary on the seige of Singapore ending with the release of the remaining skeletal-like prisoners of war from Changi, and a gigantic mushroom of thick black smoke rising over the city of Hiroshima.

'Did the Japanese ever come to make war in Australia?' I ask Kim.

'Yes, they tried, but only got as far as Darwin, though a warship was sighted in the Sydney harbour. A few soldiers managed to land in Queensland, and a handful were found in a country town of New South Wales.'

'And yet they managed to take over parts of the Phillipines, Java, Burma, and Malaya, Singapore, Hong Kong and China in succession.'

'Because these countries in south-east Asia are close to each other, and accessible by land. Asia, India, Europe are parts of one big piece of land. Australia is an isolated continent, separated by seas from other countries.'

On that vast block of land called Asia, the shadow of war had been trailing me for years, from my childhood, through my adolescence into adulthood. It threatened me in my ancestral village but I had evaded it. Fled by foot, jumped on fire-wagon, sailed in freighter from the Pearl Estuary to the Fragrant Harbour — Hong Kong — and now westward in an ocean-linear through the Dragon's Teeth Gate heading for Singapore.

The week-long journey ended as the liner moored at St John's island. Two officials came on board and inspected us for any telltale signs of illness or disease. Those with skin sores, coughing of blood or opium addiction were detained.

'They'll be quarantined there for sometime,' we were told.

We sailed again that night, and by morning reached a very busy harbour — the port of Singapore. Numerous small boats surrounded the liner, which anchored some distance from Clifford Pier. We hired two sampans, each accommodated only two passengers besides the numerous pieces of luggage. Much cheaper than the motorboats.

'You *sinkehs*?' the boatman asked us while he rowed.

'What's *sinkehs*?' we asked.

'"New guests" — newcomers — easily conned. So take care.'

Our friends Kam and Goh were at the pier to meet us. They looked darker, from exposure to the tropical sun. 'Welcome to your new country,' they greeted us.

They supervised the loading of our luggage into a bullock-drawn cart, and we squeezed two people into each rickshaw.

'To Bullock-cart-water,' Kam ordered, and explained to us: 'It's the district where we live, the name originated from the time when water was brought in tins from the reservior by bullock-carts. Now we have taps with running water in the house.'

Our new home was No 29 Temple Street in the Bullock-cart-water district. The sub-landlady was Eng, Chun's sister; Kam and Goh were tenants there. They occupied two rooms on the first floor, which was accessible by a very steep wooden staircase. Downstairs was a shop selling terra-cotta products. On this floor there was also a communal kitchen and a bathroom with a water tap and cement floor, next to a toilet of the flushing system. Our cubicle was up another floor, in an attic with a louvre window which opened to a view of the street market below. Our 'coolie's cubicle', though small, was sufficient for the four of us to sleep on the floor and pile our luggage in one corner. For many years to come, it served as our headquarters, meeting place, storage place, somewhere to rest on our days off work, or live in between jobs. We paid Eng a dollar each every three months, inclusive of electricity and water. Eng worked as a specialist amah, a 'companion' for women in their first month of confinement, the role filled by Wu Ma when Gold had her baby in the nunnery in Canton. She was booked well ahead, and in between jobs she returned to Temple Street. Her salary was double that of an ordinary amah, plus bonuses and gifts of gold as rewards. Since the post-natal woman was believed to be a carrier of ill-fortune, nobody liked to be in contact with her, so a very high salary was needed as an inducement. Chun, Eng's younger sister, worked full time and lodged and boarded at her boss's house.

The makeshift bazaar of Temple Street was a jumble of stalls and hawkers selling vegetables, meat, wet and dry provisions, and livestock of fish, fowl, reptiles and turtles.

By the end of our first month in Singapore Han and Fong, the more adventurous ones, had accepted jobs in up-country Malaya, Han as a nanny to three children of an English family in Kuala Lumpur, and Fong as a general amah, or 'one-leg-kick', with a school mistress in Seremban, capital of Negri Sembilan, one of the nine states of the Federation of Malaya. Yin was the only one to remain in Singapore and she accepted the position of housekeeper at a *mah-jong* club in Neil Road, a ten minute walk from Temple Street.

I told Kam, who went to the street market with me one day: 'I find it difficult to understand the dialects of some of the hawkers.'

'I had the same problem, it was confusing when I first arrived, but now I know a few common phrases. There are many other Chinese dialects — Hokien, Teochew, Hakka — often spoken with borrowed words from the local Malays.'

In my village of Lung Sun, in Canton and in Hong Kong, all the Chinese spoke Cantonese. If they came from other provinces of Canton, the accent from each village might differ, but we could still understand each other.

I was introduced to a *paranakan* family by Kam, to work as a domestic servant for a mistress named Dawn who was preparing to get married.

Kam accompanied me to my work interview. On the way she explained: '*Paranakan* implies a local or Straits-born Chinese family, who has been here for many generations and has adopted the native ways of life, dress, speech and food.'

'I haven't seen any Malays around here, only Indians coming in and out of their Temple, and the turbanned ones standing guard at the many goldsmith shops along South Bridge Road.'

'Malays are the indigenous people, they live in communities in their villages called the kampongs. You'll recognise them with their brown skin or complexion, and they wear a sarong, a wrap around their waist, plus a shirt top. On their New Year, Hari Raya, the men wear a velvet hat, the *songkok*, and the ladies have long scarves covering their heads. They eat with their fingers, no cutlery, out of banana leaves. And their food is very hot and spicy, cooked with coconut oil and rich in coconut milk. Later you will have to learn a few words of Malay, at least the basic vocabulary to live here, especially if you're going to work for a *paranakan* family.'

'And the *paranakans* are all Chinese?'

'There's no intermarrying between the Malays and Chinese, their religion doesn't permit them to marry a non-Muslim. You'll soon see for yourself. You address the mistress or Tai Tai as "Nonya", and the master as "Baba", be careful to get it correct and not "babi" which means pig, a derogatory term for the Malays.' Then she warned me: 'You may have difficulty in understanding Nonya Lim who speaks Malay mixed with the Chinese dialect Hokien.'

But it turned out that Nonya Lim spoke a spattering of Cantonese. 'How old are you, Silver?' she asked, with a peculiar tilt of her head, looking somewhat top-heavy with her hair piled up in a stiff lacquered high chignon, decorated with large gold hairpins as big as coffin nails.

'I'm in my twenties,' I answered as I fixed my gaze on her feet which were not bound, admiring the sandals embroidered with coloured beads in patterns. 'I was born the year the last Emperor was ousted,' I echoed Lee Sao's words.

She was chewing something which looked red when she spat out into a spittoon, even her inner lips and gums were stained a peculiar red. She said: 'That's at least twenty odd years ago.' She counted on her fingers, long and suntanned like her face. 'You must be twenty-seven? You are older than Dawn, my eldest daughter. She needs a mature companion like you, her sister Kitty is only ten.'

Nonya Lim wore a sarong, with a long-sleeved tunic of white voile edged with hand-made lace. The tunic was fastened with a chain of three brooches encrusted with diamonds. Apart from the peculiarity of her dress and coiffure, she looked a sun-bronzed Chinese. She wore no make-up on her long oval face.

On our way home I was curious to know from Kam what Nonya Lim had been chewing.

'Ah,' she explained, 'it's betel nut and lime wrapped in a leaf, a common habit among the locals. They even have a special box with compartments to accommodate the ingredients. I wonder if they get addicted to chewing it, like smoking the opium pipe . . .'

I started work the very next day. Dawn came to fetch me in a chauffer-driven car. She told me that she was preparing for her wedding, scheduled to take place in two months' time. During those two hectic months I accompanied her everywhere. To the tailor to try on her wedding gown of long white lace with beads and sequins to wear to the Registry of Marriage. And for the banquet on the nuptial night, a red satin Chinese tunic and skirt, finely embroidered, edged with silver and gold threads, made by another seamstress. From a Shanghai tailor she ordered many long *cheongsams*, mostly in shades of red. Red is an auspicious colour for happy occasions for the Chinese. And her rounds included the cobbler for hand-made leather high heel shoes of matching colours for the costumes.

The Lim family lived in two bungalows on stilts in a half-acre block in Scott Road, Bukit Timah. The complex was fenced in by a high wire-mesh backed up by shrubs and plants; an iron gate led to a concrete driveway for cars.

Last month a friend of Kim's who lives in Turramurra sold her house but kept the land for building another house in the future. The house, which rested on several short brick pillars, was removed intact all in one piece. We watched with fascination as it was towed away by a special trailer.

'They couldn't do that with your parents' bungalows in Scotts Road, they were enormous, with a front balcony, a large living-room, and four huge bedrooms . . .'

'You must show me where they were.'

'*Aiyah*, it's where the Holiday Inn and the Tropicana theatre restaurant now stand.'

'Look at this one.' Kim shows me a brochure advertising paint. It has a house raised high up, as if on a stage of wooden props.

'It's typical of some old Federation houses in Queensland, elevation keeps the house cool, as air circulates under the house, around and above it.'

I used to go under the bungalows to rummage or store things, and I had to bend my head in case I bumped it on the wooden floor above. Dawn, her siter Kitty, and little brother Michael lived in one bungalow with their parents Nonya and Baba Lim, while her uncles, Baba Two and Baba Three, and their wives and babies occupied the other bungalow, each with a nanny or baby amah.

There was a large garden with two wooden swings between the two bungalows on stilts, and at the back of the complex was a whole row of outhouses. The central room served as a dining-room, on each side were guests' rooms. The servants' quarters were at each end of the row. Ahmed, the Malay driver, and his family of three wives and six children, occupied the ones nearest to the car-porch. The other servants occupied those at the other end. We servants included a cook, a gardener and his wife who doubled up as the washing and ironing lady, and four nannies — not wet-nurses — in charge of Kitty, Michael, and the two newborn cousins of Dawn, but they roomed in with their charges in the respective bungalows.

I was allotted a shared room in the servants quarters, but Dawn insisted that I should sleep on a mat on the parquet floor of her room, until her wedding day. I helped her hang her dresses up in the wardrobe, tidy her dressing-table, and pile her many wedding gifts along a wall. She noted meticulously the names of the givers in a large book. Most gifts were gold jewellery or red-packets of good luck money, but there were also bed sheets, red blankets, pieces of embroidered material for making dresses, and vases.

'Why did you become a "comb-up?" Don't you like to get married and have your own babies?' she asked me.

'I'm not pretty like you, so I don't think any men would have chosen me for a wife. A "comb-up" was the only solution for me, homeless with a younger brother, at that time it gave me a chance to adopt three other sisters and go to work as a domestic servant. In China marriage is arranged through a matchmaker, and men demand large sums of money as dowries. I remember my Papa complaining that girls were a liability . . .'

Dawn had a lovely round face with large eyes, thick luscious eyelashes, and a dark forest of tumbling curls, the Chinese imitation of a Hollywood star as shown in Little Peacock Lien's scrapebook of movie stars.

She in her girlish way would always end her speech with a giggle. 'Did you ever have boyfriends?' she giggled.

'No, and I wouldn't like to marry either.' I didn't elaborate about my peeping-tom act with Tai Tai and Master.

'I met Peng four years ago at a school social, after that he used to telephone me and we would talk for hours. His father owns a wood-cutting factory, wood imported from Siam and is also a friend of Baba. Baba Lim and his ancestors have been importers of good quality rice from Siam for many generations.' Then with a giggle she continued: 'When I finished high school his aunt was sent on his parents' behalf, to ask Baba for my hand in marriage. We've been engaged for two years.'

'Engaged?'

'Look at my engagement ring.'

She laughed and flashed a single small stone set in gold. 'Not very big diamond. Nonya has bigger ones for me. We're in love, he writes me letters, I have only been out to socials on Christmas Eve and New Year. Nonya and Baba are very strict,' she said.

I wondered if being in love would make love-making gentler or any different from that I had seen between Master and Tai Tai. Would Peng get bored with her in time, and take a black-market mistress like Mr Xi? The law in this British colony was also 'one man one wife.' Dawn talked of romance and eternal love. Nineteen year old Dawn, an innocent giggler, was prepared to commit herself to one man for life, to bear his children, and be boss of her family unit. Even though we talked every night and giggled and laughed, I felt very separate from Dawn. Our lives were set out in opposite paths. Our destinies were different.

A week before the wedding Nonya Lim gave me leave to go with Ah Yap to the Temple to pray to Kuan Yin for Dawn and Peng. 'To grow old together, till their hair turns silver.' A traditional wish for prospective couples.

On the morning of the wedding, a chaperone for the marriage came to perform the ceremony of 'comb-down' or *sor-loc*, a ritual expressing gratitude and best wishes for the bride. Similar to the 'comb-up' or *sor-hei* of the celibacy vow, it too involved combing hair. The chaperone, a fat Chinese woman dressed in traditional tunic top and silky black pants and fanning herself with a large palm leaf fan, passed a comb through Dawn's hair. Dawn sat on a chair in her bedroom in front of the dressing-table. The chaperone chanted:

I comb-down once
Thanking our parents, the nicest pair around
I comb-down twice
For choosing a husband so sensible and wise
I comb-down thrice
With hopes that our family will grow in size

Then a beautician came and did Dawn's make-up western-style, all rosy rouge and red lipstick and eye-shadow.

Peng's arrival was announced with pomp and commotion, with people rushing in and out of Dawn's bedroom, her six best girlfriends rushed to bolt the door, while outside there was loud explosion of firecrackers. Peng's brothers, sisters, and best friends came knocking at Dawn's bedroom door demanding money — a form of dowry or ransom for the handsome bridegroom. Dawn's girlfriends negotiated the price through a slit of the opened door, and there followed bargaining from either side. After a hilarious half an hour a suitable figure was settled on — 'Nine, nine, nine', nine hundred and ninety-nine dollars. Nonya wrapped the money in a red-packet and one of the girlfriends handed it through the door, and the mob burst into the room.

'Why nine, nine, nine?' I asked Kam few days later when I returned to the coolie's cubicle.

'*Aiyah*, haven't you heard. Nine is an auspicious number for wedding and birthday, it puns with "long", hoping the marriage will last forever.'

Peng was dragged in by his mates, dressed in a pink suit with tail, a pink bowtie and cummerbund for a belt, wearing a silly top hat.

Arm in arm, the bride and groom made their way to the sitting-room. Dawn walked gingerly in her white high heels, the skirt of her white gown trailing behind her. A small white hat perched on her head, with a veil covering her face, with her other arm she was holding a bunch of red roses. They knelt down to pray to the ancestors' tablets at the altar in the sitting-room, while the chaperone helped to light joss-sticks and red candles. Then followed the tea ceremony. The chaperone poured cups of 'Dragon well' tea, and helped the newly weds offer with both hands, kneeling down, first to their parents, seated next to the altar, then to the other elders, relatives, and friends. The chaperone poured out best wishes and congratulary phrases, thanks and appreciation for all those in attendance, and in return received many red-packets for her efforts. More presents of red-packets of gold and money were given during the ceremony, and I was the keeper of these, as instructed by Nonya Lim.

Dawn's wedding was unlike any other I'd ever seen. An elaborate celebration which lasted a week. Guests came from as far as Penang and Malacca, for there were many *paranakans* in those part of Malaya. They brought with them their families and servants, and they were all accommodated in Nonya Lim's big complex and outhouses.

The celebrations would start from noon, a meal of special 'nonya' dishes: hot curries, fish marinated in coconut juice, delicacies baked in banana leaves, and a row of Malay satay hawkers fanning their charcoal braziers, grilling sticks of satays. The fragrant aroma of spices penetrated every room in the complex, and lured hungry guests down to the garden where the meal was served.

The women passed their time in gossip or in card games like dominoes called the 'four colours'. The men opted for poker or *mah-jong*. At night the real entertainment began. Children watched a puppet show while a banquet of twelve courses was laid out on twenty or more tables. Menus included exotic dishes such as braised shark's fin, bird's nests, stewed bear's paws. And on the charcoal spit suckling pigs were roasted to a crispy skin of gold hue. After dark the garden was a fairyland of light. There were two live shows, on temporary stages made of bamboo poles and attap roofs. There was a Cantonese opera, *wayang*, with players in brightly-coloured sequinned costumes and heavy exaggerated facial make-up. They sang arias in forced high-pitched tones, and fought with swords and spears, acrobats performing triple somersault to loud beatings of drums. A

Chinese orchestra in full view of the audience played instruments like the zither, *erh-hu*, flute, cymbal and gong. The *wayang* attracted a female audience, while the males crowded on stage for the *rongeng* — a Malay folk dance. And with the Malay dance-hostesses they girated, twisted, rocked forward and backward, to the rhythm of the bongo.

Peng moved into Dawn's room in the bungalow in Scott Road. I moved in with Ah Yap, the cook. My duties were to keep Dawn's bedroom clean and tidy, and wash and iron their clothes. Dawn and Peng dressed in western style clothes, she in dresses and skirts and he in shirts with ties and jacket and a hat. I wondered at what stage of their lives would they adopt the same manner of dress as Nonya and Baba, in sarong and kebaya like high-class Malays.

They joined the rest of the family for meals at a large round marble table in the main dining-room. We servants ate their leftovers, and occupied their table when they had finished eating.

Peng was driven by Ahmed to the office to work every day, but Dawn was a lady of leisure. When it suited her she learned about the baking of 'nonya' cakes and curry from Nonya Lim. Coconut milk was the main ingredient, and in some cakes they used lumps of brown sugar made from palm sap, called *gula malaka*. Sometimes she would spend her time chatting to her friends on the telephone, or would get Ahmed to drive her to Robinson or John Little at the Collier Quay. These two department stores sold goods imported from Britain, esteemed to be of high quality. I was given permission to return home to the cubicle in Temple Street at least once a week, and would telephone Ah Yin beforehand to arrange to meet her there. We would save our letters from Ah Han and Ah Fong to take them to the *siasin-loa*. It cost twenty cents of the new king money for a letter to be read and a reply written. Ah Han and Ah Fong could only return for a week on the Chinese New Year for a reunion with Yin and me. They had to travel by the fire-wagon for a night to reach Singapore.

Nine months later Dawn gave birth to Wah. She went into hospital for a week, and had a doctor and private nurses to attend her at the birth.

Nonya Lim said: 'I gave birth to all my children in this house, with the help of a midwife who lived a block away. *Aiyah*, I don't like the idea of going to the hospital . . . it's meant as a last resort, for the really helpless — terminal.'

Having a baby is also terminal, I thought, the end of the pregnancy.

I became nanny to baby Wah. When I nursed her in my arms, I thought of the days in my village when I had helped my mother to look after the younger ones. I used to strap them in a sling on my back while attending to other chores, but at night they would sleep with my mother so she could breast-feed them when they cried. Wah was fed by bottle, not on demand but every four hourly. Even if she woke up in the night crying, she was not fed until the clock said it was time. I felt very close to her, almost maternal, and treated her like my own. I sang a lullaby in Malay which Nonya Lim taught me.

Dawn had become rather quiet since the birth, she seldom talked to me except on how to nurse Wah. Dawn was educated in English, and had a booklet with instructions on how to deal with the baby in various situations. We often argued about my method, which was based on practical experience and old wives' tales. At first she didn't trust me and would often come to Wah's room to supervise me. Peng had a lot of social commitments, and often left his wife behind at home.

'Women were often segregated from men in those days,' I tell Kim. 'Even at the same function they were not seated together at the same table or in the same room.'

'They can't do that now. Here it'll be labelled as sexual discrimination. There's a complaint unit for such matters. Women have suffered long enough from such humiliation — male chauvinism.'

Before long Dawn was pregnant again. And when Wah was a year old, Dawn had her second baby, John. I became the *naima* to John also, and by this time I'd already gained a lot of experience from looking after Wah. They were both bottle-fed on canned condensed milk, which I mixed with equal portion of hot water.

When John was about six months old, there circulated rumours of the spread of war — the Japanese had gained ground in China. But China seemed a million miles away . . .

Until the events of eighth December, 1941, I wasn't convinced that the war had started here in Singapore. It had caught up with me at last.

I am by nature a light sleeper. But on that morning, the chime of the grandfather clock for half past four was drowned out by the sound of low diving planes. The house shook. Glass windows shattered. There were loud deafening explosions. Dogs barked. Startled babies and children cried. People rushed out of doors to investigate, asking each other 'What happened? What happened?'

Sirens blasted a warning through the air, screeching urgency.

I rushed to the window. The sky flashed with searchlights scanning for the enemy planes. Too late. The planes had disappeared, out of the range of the streaks of light, into the safety of darkness.

Everyone in the house was awake now. Baba and Nonya came out wrapped in their sarongs, men and women rushed into the garden, out to the road, in pyjamas and thongs in the commotion.

'Look, fire, something's burning.' Someone pointed towards the north, the direction of Bukit Timah. The sky was ablaze. Bright light dazzled my eyes.

'Bombed by the Japs,' Peng said.

Scotts Road bustled with chaotic traffic: cars and ambulance with red blinking lights, fire-engines with bells ringing. Police vans screeched round street corners. Frantic parents checked their children's safety. Neighbours consoled each other.

'It's a mistake, can't be the Japs, they wouldn't dare.'

'Singapore is impregnable. The "little myopic men" from the Eastern Ocean surely wouldn't have the audacity to defy the supreme power of the British Empire, to invade this British colony.'

We waited anxiously to hear the seven o'clock news. A tremulous voice on the radio announced the bombing of Singapore by the Japanese.

'At four thirty am. Areas hit are Bukit Timah, Chinatown, and Keppel Harbour. Buildings are still burning. The number of causalties is still uncertain.'

The *Straits Times* and the *Nanyang Sia Pao* printed pictures of damaged houses, corpses, people injured and displaced from their homes, crying by the roadside.

The whole Lim family gathered at the round table for breakfast as usual, but the grown-ups, led by Baba Lim, talked of nothing but the preparation for war, and the uncertainty ahead. They proposed to move from the Scotts Road compound, which was too open and exposed, in the event of a war. We hurriedly set about packing the valuable items: porcelain vases and dining sets, wrapping them to be buried in crates in the flowerbed. Delicate objects of value like scrolls, paintings, tapestries, embroideries, were stored under the roof, bundled in wax-coated, waterproof material.

The portable assets — gold jewellery, diamonds, jade and precious stones — were stuffed into large hidden pockets of moneybelts or vests, which every member of the family wore beneath their outer attire.

The men organised a voluntary service to build air-raid shelters, dig trenches, fill sandbags, and obtain buckets to fetch water to fight fires. They drilled and practised twice a day, helping the old and young in and out of the shelters. The cook returned from the market in Ahmed's car and urged Baba Lim to buy food to store, for there was a rush for food, and stocks were sold out quickly. People even bought live fowl, poultry, fish, pigs, piglets, goats, and dogs to rear. Tinned and canned food was purchased by the box. The price of food escalated from day to day, as stocks dwindled. Keppel Harbour was bombed again, the go-downs were burnt. Cargo ships sank.

We women at home were busy sewing — baggy loose clothes in dull colours, vests with hidden pockets for storing money and jewellery, belts with buttoned compartments — the camouflage of war. From the local silversmith identity bracelets with names, date of birth, and addresses were ordered for each member of the Lim family. I helped paste sheets or strips of old newspaper on glass windows and mirrors, with the expertise I had gained in Hong Kong. We covered lamps and lights with black material or smeared them with a black dye to blackout the light. A curfew was imposed every night. All lights were dimmed. But when the siren sounded, a full blackout was mandatory. Now I fully understand the fear that drove those countless refugees who had streamed through my once peaceful village Lung Sun. So many fears merged into one great terror: the fear of dying, of injuries, of destruction, of captivity and the subsequent humiliation and loss of freedom. And especially of rape and torture.

The shriek of sirens dictated our lives, sent us running in and out of air-raid shelters, pushing, fighting to get there first. We huddled together in the discomfort of the heat and bad smells, to be eventually set free by the siren of release. A temporary reprieve.

Eng rang me with two messages. Han had phoned from Kuala Lumpur and was about to sail with her English boss by ship to Australia. And Fong had left from Port Dickson with her boss the school-mistress, bound for India.

Yin had lost her job when the *mah-jong* club closed down. She was back at the coolie's cubicle at Temple Street.

I went with her to the wharf at Keppel Harbour, jammed with anxious and worried people who were crying or talking, holding hands, and embracing. We pushed our way onto the ship. Most passengers were European women and children. A few local prominent Chinese families were among the evacuees. Han spotted us and called out. She clutched our hands. No words were possible to express our feelings — we did not know if we would ever meet again. Our handkerchiefs were soaked with tears. Ah Han promised to write. We waved goodbye. People were hanging on to streamers from the decks. It was a very sorrowful departure. We rushed home as soon as the ship sailed, before the curfew started. The air attacks for the next two weeks were well targeted: warehouses, go-downs, the conduits for water in the Johore causeway.

But Baba Lim and Peng read in the newspapers that the British troops in Singapore were still hopeful that Churchill would send the allied troops to save them in time, and so they were out in full force celebrating Christmas, dancing and drinking at the Raffles Hotel and dining by candlelight at the Victoria Memorial Hall.

By the end of December I was accustomed to the loud blare of the sirens and could tell the various types: those warning the approach of enemy's planes, those releasing us from the shelters, those for clearance of curfew. I was used to squatting for hours in the packed air-raid shelter, clutching John with one hand and Wah with the other.

Many friends of Baba and Nonya Lim were leaving Singapore, some sailing to Indonesia, others to Ceylon, Sumatra — anywhere, away from this island. Baba said the only way of escape now was by sea. The enemy had landed in the north, Annam, and certainly would come down by land.

But Baba and his brothers were determined to stay. Their ancestors had been in Singapore for the past four generations; the pioneers. They said: 'Born and bred here and will die here'.

They had decided to move to their shop premises at Boat Quay, in the inner city, by the Singapore River. The two shop-houses, three storeys high, served as warehouses and offices. The ground floor was stacked with sacks of rice, hidden among which was an air-raid shelter. In the courtyard a few chickens, a goat, some ducks and a piglet were reared. There was a recently dug well, and a large concrete fish-tank. The second floors were converted into sleeping areas for the men. The women's quarters was under the roof to which there was no obvious access. A secret attic.

The Malay chauffeur Ahmed chose to remain in the out-house to look after the compound. Ahmed said he wasn't afraid of the Japanese, he had heard that they were friendly to the Indians and Malays, and only singled out the Chinese and Europeans to victimise. Ahmed made many trips driving us to our new home, with our bundles of clothes and boxes of provisions.

The streets were crowded with refugees from Malaya, looking for addresses of friends or relatives. Beggars and looters ransacked houses abandoned by their owners. Deserters, soldiers shell-shocked and of low morale, wandered aimlessly, dirty, unshaven and tired, searching for food. The air reeked with the smell of burning rubber. Garbage piles by the roadside were thick with flies and maggots.

Day by day the invasion seemed more imminent. There were countless bombings, more ships were sunk in the harbour. And when the warship *Prince of Wales* went down, we knew there was no hope. England could not save us from the invasion in time, because of its distance, and the Allied troops were engaged in another war in Europe. Our neighbour received a fuzzy up-country radio report of the capture of Penang. We realised it would be only days or hours before they arrived in Singapore. We were doomed. Stranded on an island. Like ants on a hot tin roof, scrambling here and there for cover, helpless and powerless. Waiting to be scorched.

From their planes the Japanese now dropped pamphlets instead of bombs, urging us to surrender peacefully, not to resist. Pamphlets of cartoons of British soldiers carrying white flags came fluttering down from the sky.

Ahmed heard rumours that people were still leaving — a last minute escape for the soldiers who had deserted, Europeans and those involved in anti-Japanese movements. They left in small fishing boats, dingies, sampans, inconspicuously drifting away. Those who stayed on burned any evidence that might endanger or jeopardise their lives such as documents and reports of war strategies and espionage. Ammunitions, armament and explosives, tanks and machinery were destroyed. Publicans smashed their stores of whisky, brandy and other intoxicating liquor, having heard news of Hong Kong's invasion at Christmas, when the Japanese soldiers got drunk and raped and killed many women.

We hid in our home with the windows shut and doors bolted. It was three days before the Chinese New Year — the year of the Horse, and it was the quietest New Year of my life. No celebrations, or firecrackers. No bombing, curfews or gunfight, no radio or newspapers. Later, many days later, we learned that the enemy had come in the middle of the night, pedalling their bicycles across the bombed causeway of the Straits of Johore. They came from the north, down the peninsula, by land, while the guns and cannons were directed south, towards the sea. They met no resistance on their way in, and occupied the Ford factory as their headquarters. They sent an ultimatum to the Governor's house.

After Singapore fell came the dreaded house call.

We had been warned and were expecting it. A routine systematic check from door to door was the enemy's excuse to look for women for the soldiers' entertainment. When heavy footsteps of boots crunched the cobbled stone, followed by the shouts of dodging street urchins, *'Ren lai lah . . . ren lai lah'*, we knew it was a signal that the enemy was approaching. We women squeezed into the secret attic and lay in silence, waiting, listening, holding our breaths. The children were lightly gagged, to muffle their cries, for the sound of children would betray the presence of their mothers.

There were no windows, and right under the roof, we were in the direct path of the heat of the tropical sun.

I felt beads of perspiration running down my face. Bad breath, body odour, and stinking sweat filled the air. My heart was pounding. A loud kick on the wooden door nearly knocked my heart out of my ribcage.

Bang bang bang. The sound of door creaking. Shouts in Japanese. Someone in a high-pitched voice translated: 'How many in the family?'

'Six. Myself, my two brothers and two sons and a male coolie.'

'The names?' And Baba Lim rattled off the information requested. 'What about the *koniens*?'

'They remained in the kampong.'

'Any *koniens* here?'

'None here. Gone to kampong. Had the smallpox with their kids.'

'Smallpox — contagious.'

The high-pitched voice was heard again in the enemy's language, interspersed with '*Hai, hai . . .*'

'You are to report to the *Kempeitai* tomorrow morning for registration. Understand? Punctual at nine at Raffles Boys' School.'

'Bow, bow low, bend down low, three bows to the officers.'

'*Hai. Hai.*'

The footsteps faded. The creaking door closed. A heavy

bolt slammed. Nonya Lim fainted, someone was applying tiger-balm on her. The cook vomited. Sour smell of stale food. I felt sick, but fought back the surge of saliva and fluid.

John pulled out his gag and I stuck his bottle into his mouth.

The trapdoor was opened, and we were helped down by Peng and Ah Sun the coolie. Baba gave Nonya Lim some smelling salts to revive her. I was glad the house call had finished. The angel of death had passed.

But the following day brought a new worry for the men: the *Kempeitai*, the secret police. The men left at eight o'clock to report as ordered.

Only the women and children stayed behind. The cook bolted the door and shut all the windows. We dressed in our drab loose clothes, knotted our hair into buns, and smeared our faces with soot to make ourselves look unattractive. We trod softly indoors like ghosts.

Michael returned by himself in the early afternoon. He said Ah Sun, the coolie had been taken away in a different lorry from that of the three Babas and Peng. Michael was ordered to leave because he was under-age, only ten years old. Lots of men were driven away in lorries, he said.

We waited, not daring to venture outdoors to talk to the neighbours. The three Nonyas were too worried to eat. Dawn asked me to pray to their ancestors' tablet on the altar for the safe return of the men. Another day dragged on. Then, the next day, Ah Sun staggered in, weak, delirious and sunburnt. When he recovered he told us of his narrow escape. The lorry had taken him to a beach. He had an urgent 'nature call' and they had let him go to a toilet nearby. But it was too dirty and smelly so he wandered off to the bush. From his squatting position, he had witnessed the massacre — the men from the lorry were forced to wade into the sea, and were shot point-blank from behind. They fell down, colouring the water red. Ah Sun was so shocked, that he lost control of his motions. He stumbled home, dazed and with no notion of time. From then on he lost control of his motions whenever he saw a Japanese.

That evening the three Babas and Peng also returned in a bullock cart, driven by Ahmed. They had been taken to some barracks, previously used by the British troops, and left there for the night. Peng and the three Babas hid in a broom closet. They heard the soldiers come back to shout orders for everyone to leave. Four lorry-loads of men were driven away. When all was quiet they crept out of the closet and ran from the deserted barracks. On their walk home, they had passed Scotts Road and rested there. Ahmed cooked them a meal and drove them home in a borrowed bullock-cart. The Nonyas gave me a big hug — my prayers to their ancestors had been answered.

Ahmed had been given a protection and travel permit written in Japanese which bore a red seal. A reward for playing host to some Japanese officers and his soldiers. The uninvited guests had stayed at Baba Lim's bungalows on stilts for a week when they first arrived on the island.

Ahmed had borrowed this bullock-cart from his Indian friend to visit his relatives in Bedok and Changi, as petrol was no longer available. He described the crowd of British troops and civilians in the Padang who were ordered to walk all the way to Changi prison. Many collapsed with heatstroke.

'Too hot for the *putehs* as they had never walked for so long, always travelled in the car.'

'And the women go to Changi too?' Peng asked.

'Ladies and children were taken to the Great World.'

Which was an amusement park with shops, theatres, cabaret and shooting gallery and ghost train . . .

So began the Japanese Occupation. Although we stayed indoors, I couldn't help peeping out of the windows. I witnessed the horrors of torture and humiliation that ranged from face-slapping to kicks in the stomach or forced feeding with water-hose. From Babas, Peng and Ah Sun we learned of the daily atrocities committed in the streets of Singapore: the public displays of severed heads stuck on spikes of garden fences, haloed with flies. They served as a deterrent against future lootings. It was a reign of terror and brutality.

We worried about the violation of our bodies by the enemy. By day we hid and slept, crammed under the roof in the baking heat. As night-stalkers we came out in the dark when everyone else was asleep. We groped for a match to light a joss-stick and prayed quietly to the ancestors' tablet for continuous protection. We sneaked into the courtyard, where the toilet and bathrooms were, to empty the urinals, to wash ourselves. And to cook meals by candlelight. Time eluded us, we creatures of the night, of darkness, leading a clandestine life. Many months slipped by before we women were gradually persuaded to come out of hiding.

'The Japanese have changed their attitude,' the men assured us. 'They no longer torture people in the streets. Many schools and shops are reopened and offices have resumed work.'

Life during the Occupation in Syonan Tao — the Island of Southern Lights — the new name of Singapore, held many confusions. I was baffled by the cocks crowing at eight in the morning, and the sun setting at nine at night! Time had been altered to follow Tokyo's, a leap forward of three hours. The only relic left of colonial Singapore was the bronze statue of Sir Stamford Raffles, which proved too heavy and cumbersome to be moved. The new currency — the 'banana notes' — devalued so rapidly from day to day, that it was carried in bundles in rice sacks. And the local newspapers, the *Straits Times* and the *Nanyang Sia Pao*, ceased to exist; taking their place was *Syonan Tao Sinbun*, printed in Katakana and Hiragana, with occasional Han-Ji.

I ventured out of doors. The Boat Quay was a bustle of activity. Coolies were unloading the remaining cargo from the *tongkangs* supervised by Ah Sun. They used a hook to lift each sack on to their shoulders. The hook tore a hole which left a trail of grain along their path, attracting beggars, street urchins, scavengers who crouched and fought each other for the rice. There was much pushing and jostling, shouting and arguing. Ah Sun shooed them off as the scuffling interrupted the work of the coolies. Ah Sun would still tremble at the sight of a Japanese soldier and soil his pants.

The Singapore River was black; its mirrored surface occasionally rippled by a breeze which rocked its flotsam of animal carcasses, bloated human bodies and their dismembered and gangrenous parts, and other bits and pieces of inorganic garbage. Into the hot and still air rose a strong stench redolent of decay and putrifaction. In Syonan Tao, such smells were everywhere, in rubbish piles at street corners, and blocked monsoon drains. In bombed-out sites weeds grew amongst piles of rubble, and flies, maggots and rats made their nests in the refuse.

I took a day off to visit my sister Yin at Temple Street. It wasn't possible to communicate by phone, the lines were manned by Japanese-speaking operators and conversation couldn't proceed further than utterances of '*Moshi Moshi* (hello).'

Ah Sun hailed me a trishaw — a contraption consisting of a rickshaw, minus its shafts, attached to a bicycle on one side. The fare was negotiated prior to the journey — half a cigarette tin of rice each way. 'Banana notes' were useless. Nobody would accept them. So the barter system was used instead. The trishaw pedaller extolled the ingenious invention of his vehicle, how it had started soon after the birth of Syonan Tao as an energy-saving device. It was less exhausting to pedal a bicycle, especially uphill, than drag on foot a loaded rickshaw. Motor vehicles were only used by the Japanese and few were seen on the road, petrol was not available to the public. Along the five-foot way many vagabonds slept on their beds of cardboard, mats or *charpol*. They stared with hollowed eyes, apathetic and malnourished: the refugees, the orphaned, the widowed. The children did not smile. Their faces were dirty, their scanty hair matted and riddled with lice. There was no charity kitchen to sustain them. I felt abundantly rich, secretly armed with five cigarette-tins of rice, one for my trishaw-fare, the others for my sister Yin and our friends Kam, Goh, Eng and Chun, whom I hadn't seen since the day of Han's departure.

Food stalls were conspicuously absent in the makeshift market of Temple Street. Instead there were stalls staffed by ordinary householders displaying their possessions: cloth, shoes, slippers, for barter or exchange for food. Yin was among them. She sat in a corner opposite the letter-writer in front of the pottery shop of 29 Temple Street.

'Yin, how are you?' I cried with joy at the sight of her.

She was unpicking a cotton thread from an old bedspread, and using it to stitch the patchwork of her quilt.

'Ah Silver! We have been very worried about you, not a

word for months.' Her tears fell onto the finished quilt folded neatly by her feet as she sat on a low wooden stool. 'We sent messengers to enquire and were told that you were in the kampong.'

I asked: 'How's business?'

Her face brightened. 'I've traded two quilts, one for two live chicks, and the other for tapioca, sweet potatoes and yam.'

'How are the others?'

'Kam and Eng are jobless. But they make nets for the fishermen from a fibre made from dried pineapple, in exchange for a few fish, squid or prawns. Now they're queueing for their weekly ration of rice and meat down the road . . .'

'I've brought you some rice.'

'Really?' The gleam of joy in her eyes was wonderful to see. 'Of course, your boss is a rice dealer. Let's go upstairs.'

I helped her gather her quilts while she packed away the needles and thread and the bamboo stool. We climbed the steep staircase, and when we reached the dining-table on the first floor I produced the four tins from the inner pockets of my vest. I opened each tin and showed her the brown and white varieties.

'Our family doctor advised the brown unpolished rice to ward off swelling of the legs and feet, Beri Beri, as he calls it.'

'The "leg air".' Yin pulled up her trousers to show me her puffy legs. '*Aiyah*, the rice from the ration is limited to half a katie a month per head. We spend hours isolating the grains of rice from the mixture of sand and stones and seeds.'

In the kitchen, two chicks chirped in a box. 'They grow fast and plump on the cockroaches that come out at night.'

Kam and Eng returned with their weekly quota of adulterated rice. They were delighted to see me and most grateful for the tins of rice.

'Today we'll celebrate our reunion with a special lunch.'

We had rice — the good clean rice I brought — boiled with sweet potato, and sliced tapioca and yam.

Kam lamented: 'We can't get any cooking oil, so every dish is boiled, nothing can be fried.

'It's the same in every household,' I assured her.

'There is red palm oil and coconut oil. But of course they're not as nice as peanut or olive oil . . .' Eng reminisced. 'Besides, there's no meat to fry, all we get from our ration is skin and bones.'

'We can have eggs when the chicks grow.' Yin tried to cheer them up.

'What I miss most is soap. Good thing now we wear dark colour . . . 'And they related how they too had hidden and dodged the Japanese during the first few months of the Occupation.

Peng made soap from a formula in his chemistry book. It didn't lather much. Still it got rid of grease.

'I'll bring you a cake of home-made soap next time I come,' I told my sisters. Survival, the will to live, made us resourceful. We looked for substitute of the essentials. Only in my childhood days in Lung Sun, in the face of natural disasters — earthquakes, deluge, drought — were we powerless and helpless.

My trishaw came to fetch me home some six hours later. I reserved him for the same time, same day, the following week — same fare.

Baba Lim's family were very lucky to have a large courtyard which was turned into a menagerie: a concrete tank for fish, a nanny goat, a piglet in a wicker pigsty, and a few rooster and hens which laid eggs and hatched chicks. Our gardener, who returned to his kampong, often brought us sweet potatoes, yams and vegetables in exchange for some rice. He helped us start our own nursery, planting in pots or boxes. Soon we had a colourful collection of green spring onions, red tomatoes, and chilli plants. Our nanny goat was milked every day, our only milk supply as we had finished the condensed milk. We made paper from compressed dry grass, but it was of very rough texture, it hurt when used as toilet paper.

'Better than nothing,' Ah Sun reminded us.

Our piglet became a full grown pig, and during the third year of the Japanese Occupation Ah Sun slaughtered it for the Chinese New Year Festival dinner. Every part of the pig was eaten, including its ears, tongue and blood. Its skin was dried and deep-fried, a crispy crunchy delicacy. We gave up eating bread when wheat flour was exhausted. The substitute of tapioca flour made the bread hard like brick. With a large granite hand-grinder we ground soy bean with water. In this way we made tofu and soya bean milk. We even had surplus to sell.

Ahmed came at least once a month for rice and gave us news. He was able to make contact with our English family doctor — Dr Thompson — who was a prisoner of war in Changi.

'Thin and yellow, all skin and bones, a living skeleton.'

'Please take more rice and cook some for him,' Dawn implored, for Dr Thompson was her personal physician, who had delivered John and Wah, and was a great friend of the family.

'I smuggled him *ikan nasi* when the guard wasn't looking. They are taken to work on a site, digging and turning soil.

Lucky he wasn't taken to work on the railway . . .'

One day all *towkays*, including Baba Lim, were summoned to the Japanese headquarters by order of General Yamaguchi. As owner of the Scotts Road property, he had to pay a large sum of money in tax into a Japanese Bank which had just opened up in Singapore.

Peng heard from his colleague in the financial trade that the Japanese military planned to extract a sum of fifty million Straits dollars (value of old British currency) from the local Chinese of Singapore and Malaya. Baba Lim and his brothers were forced to pawn their antiques, and mortgage the Scotts Road property and the shop-houses at Boat Quay. Many opportunists became rich during this time, buying up antiques and jewellery and properties at rock-bottom prices to sell at a later date at an appreciated value. There was corruption and bribery. Black-market bloomed.

Silence . . . A whole day slipped by followed by a night of darkness, calm and still. No barking of dogs, only the scurrying of mice, or *chi-chak* (wall lizards) chirping. Not a soul in the streets. All the doors of houses barred, the shutters of windows down. Where are the Japanese soldiers who patrol the streets? Have they disappeared? Gone to conquer another country?

Another dawn without any siren to end the night curfew. This was most unusual and unnerving. Restless and curious I came out of hiding, stretched myself and tiptoed to the windows to peep through the shutters. The neighbours too were peeping, creeping. Gradually they sneaked out through the back door into the alleys, looking furtively to the right and left. Then with more confidence they moved to the front of the houses, the main streets. Soon every family opened their doors and flung wide their windows, breathing in the hot odorous air. Flies buzzed into houses and dashed against walls. By noon people had spilled onto the streets, talking freely, speculating as to the whereabouts of the soldiers who had controlled us for three and a half years.

Suddenly there was a droning noise, a helicopter swooped and showered pamphlets. They landed everywhere, on roofs, gutters, pavements, roads, rubbish piles. People were at first transfixed, then scattered about picking up the pamphlets.

'It's in wriggling writing!' Ah Sun shouted.

Peng read aloud: 'The Japanese have surrendered unconditionally. The British are returning. They say don't do anything rash in the meantime until the Interim Government arrives.'

'Hurray! Hurray!'

People jumped for joy, clutching the pamphlets. Some burst out laughing, others clapped their hands, or screamed with relief. The street was filled with loud chatterings. Everyone talked at the same time, echoing the message: 'The dwarfs have left, I can't believe it's true . . .' Some ran inside the houses to tell the elderly folks, others rushed out to see their neighbours and friends, embracing them, shaking and holding their hands, slapping their backs, joking, and crying. The butcher opened his shop and produced a leg of salted meat, shouting his invitation: 'Come on everyone, let's celebrate with a slice of smoked ham each. I've been saving it for such an occasion'. Other neighbours carried out a barrel of rice wine and poured into a large bowl and the men flocked round and had a sip each. We women came out in our loose clothes, rubbed the soot from our faces, and started to compare our tales of woe. The old inched their way out on their walking sticks smiling toothlessly. Grandmothers with small bound feet hobbled unsteadily, leaning on their grandchildren for support. The barber appeared with his harmonica and I joined his wife and daughters, dancing in the street and singing a local song.

A.B.C.
Let's hurry
To Fatimah
For curry.

D.E.F.
You'll get fat
On ikan nasi
And Chapati.

X.Y.Z.
Don't tell me
Ali and Babi
Are going to marry.

Somebody lit firecrackers, and the children cavorted, cried, screamed, giggled, and wailed as loudly as they wanted. No more muffles, gags or suppression. Their first taste of freedom. The street throbbed and pulsated with noisy people. The houses gaped with vast emptiness. And that was how the Japanese Occupation came to an end, on the twelfth of September, 1945.

Later that week the *Straits Times* and the *Nanyang Sia Pao* resumed printing, and showed pictures of a tall mushroom cloud reaching up to the sky. Peng said that the Americans had dropped an atomic bomb on Hiroshima, with devastating effects on the Japanese people. Apart from the usual destruction of houses and lives, the survivors suffered severe burns. The prisoners of war were released from Changi, and transferred to the General Hospital, staffed once again by qualified doctors. Many running-dogs and traitors left the island — those who had betrayed their own people to the Japanese, been involved in bribery and black-market. They headed for Hong Kong and Formosa.

Baba Lim managed to live to see the British flag fly again. He died three months after the liberation, from typhoid. Nonya Lim knew Baba had never really recovered in spirit since the day he had mortgaged his properties, and sold his treasures.

Those who had fled before the colony fell had started to return. Ah Han and Ah Fong came back with their bosses. After a brief stopover in Singapore, they all returned to their previous residences in up-country Malaya. Yin resumed her job at the *mah-jong* club in Neil Road. We continued to retain our coolie's cubicle in Temple Street, sharing with Chun, Eng, Kam and Goh.

It took another two years before life returned to normal. Inflation was high; there were no imports for months. Shortages of meat, food, and medicinal products persisted. The warehouses and the docks were in ruins and roads were full of pitholes. Derelicts were everywhere. Although schools, offices and business resumed a few months after the liberation, the shops were not stocked with food for a long time.

Baba Two and Baba Three and their families moved to rented flats. Nonya Lim and the cook Ah Yap went to live with her elderly mother. Dawn and Peng rented a two-bedroom place at Moulmein Road. The children and I shared one room. But the relationship between Peng and Dawn was strained.

'I'm very worried for myself, Ah Silver, Peng comes home so late every night, drunk and rowdy.'

'It's his business social commitments?'

'It's not healthy to quarrel in front of the children, but I can't stand him womanising outside. And my "horsy" is late this month, what shall I do?'

'Why don't you consult Dr Thompson? He might be able to help you regulate the "horsy", with some medicine.'

Dawn believed in western medicine, so I couldn't very well recommend the herbalist-physician.

But Dr Thompson had bad news for her. She was pregnant again.

'I begged him to help me get rid of this baby but he wouldn't listen to me. I've told him frankly the relationship between Peng and myself is very shaky . . .'

'Keep the baby,' I urged her. 'The baby won't worsen the relationship between you and Mr Peng.'

'He hasn't come home for three days now. How can I go on carrying his baby?' she cried.

'But it's yours too. I think you're more involved in breeding the baby than he, have courage, carry on. My mother had sixteen pregnancies.'

But quietly she went to consult a Malay *bomoh*, a witch doctor, who was reputed to have a formula to rid babies with fruit juices.

Dawn resorted to drinking a concotion of pineapple and watermelon juice in an attempt to abort the baby. She only stopped drinking when she felt the baby move.

Kim was born a 'blue baby' at the K.K. hospital.

'She has a hole in the heart,' Dr Thompson diagnosed. 'Needs a closure operation.'

I nursed the new baby, as John and Wah attended primary school. I bought pigs' and chickens' hearts and chopped them into pieces to cook soup or steam them in porridge. I chewed the heart muscle before spoon-feeding it into her little mouth. Traditionally the Chinese believed that if you had a defect in a particular organ, you could compensate by eating the animal's equivalent organ in your diet.

One day as usual I was feeding Kim with a spoonful of minced heart meat which I had chewed and regurgitated from my mouth. This upset Dawn greatly. She shouted: '*Aiyah*, don't you ever feed my baby with anything contaminated with your saliva.' Dawn snatched the spoon from me and threw it into a bin. 'Don't you know it's not hygienic?'

'This is the way babies are fed in China, in my village, in the House of Tang . . .'

'That's why tuberculosis was so rampant. Don't you ever do that to Kim again.'

I apologised, but I could not hold back my tears, for though naive and ignorant, I meant well. Dawn spoke more softly.

'Mince the meat with the edge of the chopper, and cook it well, Kim is delicate, she can't afford to contact any disease with a hole in her heart. Medicine is still hard to come by, especially penicillin, the miracle drug. When she's older, about seven years or so, I'll arrange for her to fly to Australia for a heart closure operation.'

Kim got breathless easily on exertion, and her lips would turn very blue, her heart would thump fast against her small chest wall. Her nails too were always of a bluish hue, and she knew it and wanted me to paint them with Dawn's nail polish to camouflage the real colour. We had fun painting her nails, experimenting with different shades of red, even on her toenails, and she would smudge lipsticks on her blue lips while Dawn was out.

'She's having an inferiority complex, at her age, three and

a half years old!' I thought of Ah Sai at three, with two snots running down his nose, chewing raw peanuts, drinking soup of boiled roots of weeds.

'China is still at war, with itself.' Dawn read from the *Straits Times*. 'Mao Tse-tung has emerged as the leader of the Communists, and the peasants are looking to him for salvation. Starvation and poverty are everywhere . . . Do you still have any relatives in China?'

'My third brother, but I don't know if he's still alive, no news from him since he went left the village, to go underground.'

'*Aiyah*, hundreds of thousands of people died in the Long March, which started in 1934 . . . ' Dawn said.

'My youngest brother Ah Sai is in Hong Kong, we correspond very rarely. Yes, I do know somebody called Lee Sao in China. She helped me to become a "comb-up", I owe her for what I am today. I wonder how she is.'

'Can't you write to her?'

'Ah Han is Lee Sao's niece, she's occasionally in contact with her, but its hard to get messages through, the way things are in China.'

News of China upset me, news of war, starvation, poverty, flood, epidemics. I had been through them and I knew how agonising the suffering would be. And I thought of the brother who had left us after burying mother. Would I recognise him on the street if I saw him now? After all these years I was ready to forgive him and to accept him, my long lost brother, he who had scolded us girls with foul words and treated us like slaves.

Dawn would feed me snippets of news about developments in China.

'Mao and Chou En-lai are dominating the headlines. The

communists have captured Tientsin, Shanghai, Peking. Chiang Kai-shek is losing hold on China.'

Dawn read out to me: 'Chiang Kai-shek of the Kuomintang Party retreated to Formosa with his troops. On first of October, China becomes the Communist People's Republic of China.' That was 1949.

'And how does this affect the common people?'

'The peasants are behind Mao, it should benefit the majority, improve their standard of living, they claim to have been exploited by their landlords in the past.'

There were changes in Dawn's household too. Peng had left home.

'I saw him with a European women holding hands entering a taxi,' Dawn said after returning from a shopping spree at High Street. 'Wah has seen him too.' She consulted with Kitty, who was in her first year of university, studying Law. Kitty advised her to apply for a divorce, on the grounds of desertion and adultery, and he would have to pay her maintenance for the three children.

But Peng refused to grant her a divorce.

'I think he's waiting to get half your legacy,' Kitty said.

'According to my lawyer, Peng and I have to live separately for five years before a divorce is granted on irreconcilable grounds.' Dawn told me. 'I need your support most at this time of my life, to help me cope with the children. I'll do the cooking and go to the market, but I hate washing up. Ha, ha.' She giggled for the first time in many years.

'You can count on me to stay and help you with the children,' I assured her. 'If you're tight with money, don't worry about paying me now.'

I had been nursing the three children since their births, waking up in the night, making their formula for feeding, changing nappies, soothing them through their illnesses, caring for them like my very own. The most demanding one was Kim, blue and frail, and very spoilt, still I gave her all the love and care she needed. Dawn was only interested in dressing them up and buying playthings, imported toys, and helping their learning process, she never changed their nappies or fed them, not once. She relied on me for all that. But she was a very strict mother, like Nonya Lim, and taught her children proper behaviour and good manners. Although very westernised in her education and outward appearance, she was at heart very Chinese, and believed in filial obedience and piety.

When Dawn's divorce came through five years later, she was given the sum bequeathed to her by Baba Lim.

'I'm taking Kim to Sydney for a heart closure operation, as arranged by Dr Thompson. Kitty is accompanying me. I'm placing Wah and John entirely in your charge,' she told me. 'Phone Michael at Nonya Lim if you need any help in English, he's a big lad now, he's their uncle too.'

'How long will you be gone?'

'Don't know, perhaps three months or longest six months, depending on how the operation goes. If uncomplicated, we'll be home earlier.'

So Dawn was prepared to spend most of her money on little Kim, hoping to make her whole, enabling her to lead a normal life. A noble mother's sacrifice.

And for a girl!

Kim says: 'It's one child per family in China, and as most families want a boy, guess what they do to the girls?'

'I know too well,' I reply. 'Even when there was no limit set on the number of children one could bear.'

She continues reading from *TIME* magazine: 'In the backlanes and alleys of Canton, it's not uncommon to find corpses of female babies wrapped in rags in the gutters.'

'My own mother had smothered a few. Girls weren't worth anything.'

'And you said my mother spent the greater part of her inherited money on my operation to save me, and yet she tried to abort me at the beginning. How fickle could she be.'

'Only by force of circumstances.'

'Look!' Kim shows me a very old copy of the *Woman's Weekly*. Inside is an article that featured her and Dawn in a ward of a Sydney hospital after her heart operation. It was very uncommon in those days for an Asian to venture out to Australia, and perhaps she was the first case they had had from overseas since the war.

'That's me and that's Mother and Auntie Kitty.'

'Yes, I remember your mother brought one of these home.' The photo shows the three of them happy, smiling, the operation a success.

'I also received a card drawn by you while you were recovering in hospital, and I took it to the *siasin-loa* to read. You drew a koala bear and wrote to tell me you'd be returning home earlier than anticipated. Your mother brought home boomerangs, a large koala for Wah and a kangaroo for John.'

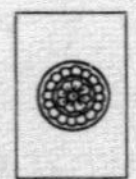

Kim returned home three months after the operation, her blueness dispelled forever. And she had grown plump and rosy in the cheeks, even her chest was more fleshy, but adorned with a long red scar across the left side. Dr Thompson said: 'Don't treat her like a delicate doll or wrap her in cottonwool. Now that her circulation is normal, she can play sports and later even bear the strain of labour for children.'

Gradually Peng's maintainence payments became more irregular, less frequent, and then he defaulted altogether, having moved to an unknown address. Dawn was feeling the financial strain. I expected the inevitable.

'I can't afford to employ you any more, Ah Silver, I can't be too selfish, and stop you from earning more money elsewhere. Now that Kim is twelve, and healthy and robust; Wah and John are teenagers and can look after themselves, I should be able to manage by myself.'

But after more than eighteen years of service with Dawn, I felt most reluctant to leave.

'Come and visit us whenever you can,' she said. 'We're close, like sisters.'

I went back to my coolie's cubicle at Temple Street, my retreat, room of my own. My neighbourhood had become a slum. The familiar two or three storey shop-houses stood neglected, with peeling paintwork, missing roof-tiles, and broken windows, waiting for demolition by the Government Urban Development Board. High-rise apartments sprang up on the outskirts of Chinatown, and rehousing people from the slums was a big and ambitious project of the Government.

It seemed to me that the Government of Singapore had become over-enthusiastic, not content to demolish and rebuild the bombed-out sites, but determined to eradicate altogether the old pre-war houses of Singapore, as though ashamed of the past. The Government seemed eager to acquire a new and modern image by wiping out its slums, re-housing all Singaporeans in new high-rise blocks, and relocating the bazaars and street markets in new supermarkets and department stores, despite protests by the owners and criticism from the tourists.

I watched the old landmarks of Singapore crumbling around me. The shop-houses in Boat Quay, including the one with a secret attic which served as my hiding place for two years, stood neglected, earmarked for demolition. The *tongkangs* in the Singapore river were towed away, the river cleared of its jetsam and waterway traffic, gradually became clean and unpolluted. I missed the saltish stale smell of rubber, most distinct at the Kallang basin where the Goodyear factory used to be, and the bustle of the loading and unloading goods at Boat Quay, the coolies crowding and lining for work, then with sacks of rice hooked and slung over their shoulders, walking the planks from the *tongkangs*, with a certain spring in their step. And in the evening the shouts of hawkers along the walkway of Boat Quay, to attract the attention of the tired coolies.

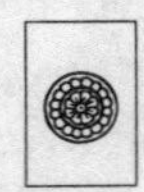

'It's now called Riverside,' Kim says, 'Singapore wants to have a clean image of its river to attract the tourists. Most cities in the world boast of their rivers, Paris the Seine, Shanghai the WangPo, so like the Bund along the WangPo, the Singapore River has its walkway: the Riverside.'

'But the Government was too drastic. In demolishing houses of character built in the pre-war style and erecting new, modern ones, they have totally removed its original colour and atmosphere.'

'So also in Canton or Kwangzhou, the riverside is cleared of opium dens and brothels . . . It's inevitable, with the march of time and progress,' Kim says. 'Although Australia is really serious about preserving its heritage under the National Trust.'

We drive to Haberfield and Burwood where Kim points out many quaint houses of unique architecture of a certain era. They are protected under the National Trust, their outward appearances cannot be altered. Kim's apartment is a good example: its facade of sandstone dated 1920 is preserved, with a new fourteen storey block built behind it.

But I found comfort in the old and the familiar and was upset by any changes. Like the row of 'death houses' for instance, in the street opposite Temple Street, on the other side of the Marianam Temple, demolition of which was specially expedited. They instantly became a tourist attraction. 'Your last chance to view these unique death houses,' called the opportunists.

The dying lay next to their coffins, gasping for breath, lapsing into coma. Foreign visitors gawked at these gloomy dark houses, where the rasping of death rattles filled the air. The funeral rites were performed on the ground floor at the shop-front, with theatrical pomp and ceremony, hired wailers and monks burning paper money, and colourful effigies of servants, houses and cars.

'When these "death houses" are gone, where will the dying

go?' The Chinese didn't like the idea of someone lingering at home, waiting to die.

'Into the hospital or at home,' Chun said. 'They're building special houses for the wake, called funeral parlours.'

But it wouldn't be the same, nothing could replace the curious old 'death houses' which had existed for years, long before I had come to Singapore. For the people of Old Singapore, a specific tradition was sacrificed in the name of progress.

Fires broke out in several parts of Chinatown, hastening the demolition of slums.

'The slums were death traps and fire hazard . . .' the media reported. 'In each house lived twenty to forty people, sharing communal toilets — bucket system — and kitchens with numerous open-fire braziers . . '

A crowded part of Neil Road was burnt out. Another fire consumed the crammed and cluttered night stalls of the 'Blue Sky market' along North Bridge Road, within walking distance of Temple Street. Stall-keepers suffered great loss as they were not insured. Who would insure a stall of cardboard partition with a roof of plastic sheeting? The Government offered to relocate them in new shops on the ground floor of the high-rise blocks, secure and fire-proof, but with high rental.

Yin's place of work, the *mah-jong* club, was damaged by water and smoke. Yin and the other victims were re-housed by the Urban Development Board in a new satellite town — Redhill — in one of the new high-rise apartments, self-contained with toilets and kitchen, with elevators and fire exit stairways. Yin never got used to her new home; always at a loss in such a complex of blocks. They were labelled in alphabets and romanised numbers. Illiterate Yin became homebound, and refused to leave the apartment unless accompanied.

Our four friends Chun, Eng, Kam and Goh wanted to return to Hong Kong for three months. I stayed in 29 Temple Street during their absence, and did Kam's job of cooking two meals, lunch and dinner, for about twenty workers in a goldsmith shop within walking distance. The salary was double that I had earned from Dawn. During my free time in the mornings, I would visit Dawn and help her with her chores, while she filled me in on the children's progress at school. Wah was eighteen and had finished secondary school. She had decided to become a teacher, and was enrolled in the Teachers' Training College of Singapore. John was in his final year of school leaving certificate.

Ah Han's boss and family had returned to England for six months, for their long overdue home leave, and Ah Han came down to Singapore to live at Temple Street. When our four friends returned from Hong Kong, praising the joy of reuniting with their old friends and relatives left behind before the war, we too felt restless, and enquired about a possible visit to China to see Lee Sao, behind the 'bamboo curtain' as it was known. We managed to obtain our visas because of our age: over forty-five. This was in 1958, and in my passport application, my age was forty-six, and I was the youngest of the four sisters. Ah Fong took leave from her boss, and we were busy preparing for our journey. Ah Han had been corresponding with Lee Sao, and had received a shopping list of the things she desperately needed: basic essentials such as clothes, shoes, blankets, soap, and even light bulbs. All mail was censored in China, and Lee Sao didn't dare express too openly the current happenings there. We tried to read between the lines, to work out what her life was really like.

We were hungry for any news of China and tuned in frequently to the radio for news in Cantonese. We heard that a system of rationing was in place, and that coupons were alloted on merits of points gained from work.

'*Aiyah*, how can Lee Sao work at her age? She's at least seventy-five.' Ah Han cried at the thought of it.

She scanned many magazines especially those imported from Hong Kong. She told us that farmland had been redistributed to the peasants, the *lao pai sin*, meaning the hundred surname or the common people, the landowners or rural gentry class destroyed.

'But,' Ah Han read on with excitement, 'listen to this. Opium or drug is not on, women are released from their status as chattel, and treated as equal to men, no concubinage, no prostitutes, and all sing-song girls are being re-educated and reformed and sent to work in factories and farms.'

This gave us hope of a new and fair China, as we still nursed the idea of returning to our ancestral land to retire in our old age.

We sailed in a freighter to Hong Kong. The journey took five days. We were at the mercy of the tail-end of a typhoon, and my three sisters were seasick and bedridden. I attended on them with hot towels and tiger-balm, and with hefty tips the steward brought them porridge and soup.

When we reached Victoria Harbour we could hardly believe our eyes. A jungle of massive high-rise with twinkling neon lights and bold coloured signboards of advertisement. Many pedestrians, dressed in sophisticated European attire, and young people in denim jeans and T-shirts. Older women had their hair cut straight or permed short. Only few of the very old ones retained their pigtails or chignon. And even young men had their hair waved! *Cheongsam*, the national dress, was only worn by waitresses in posh restaurants.

The few rickshaws at the Star ferry pier were reserved for the tourists. I couldn't trace any of the six sedan-chair bearers from the House of Tang who had come to make a living as rickshaw pullers in Hong Kong.

We were considered as the repatriates, the Overseas Chinese, having made it rich, now returning to our ancestral village, to visit friends and relatives with anticipations of future retirement. This was the ultimate wish of all Chinese who left China in their youth, to return to their place of birth to die and be buried there.

We stayed in the same guest house I had stayed in many years ago when I had first landed in Hong Kong. It specially catered for the repatriates, and offered an excellent service arranging our tickets, accommodation and itinerary in China.

While in Hong Kong I tried to make contact with Ah Sai. In one of his previous letters he had informed me: 'The head of my Society had been arrested for drug trafficking, and is now in jail. It was in the newspapers, big headlines, sister Ah Han might have come across it. My society has since been disbanded. I am glad to tell you, Ah Pah, that I'm now free, my membership is automatically dissolved.'

My *siasin-loa* replied for me: 'I'm very pleased to hear of the end of your involvement with the Triad. Be a good citizen now, try to get a decent job. Don't ever get involved in such society again.'

In another letter, his *siasin-loa* wrote: 'I'm now working in a restaurant as a sharks' fin cleaner/washer which demands a special technique, and I receive a good salary. Last month I got married to a waitress from the same restaurant, and enclosed is our wedding photo . . .'

Ah Sai looked old and stooped in the photo, no longer the tall, lanky lad with the sleek hairdo. His wife had the appearance of someone thrifty and dressed modestly, unlike the locals who seemed to go for the latest fashion, and wear the latest hairdo. I was glad for his sake, and sent him a generous sum of money to buy her some gold jewellery.

I knew that Ah Sai and his wife had adopted a little girl aged three, as soon as he had learned he was infertile, due to some childhood disease he had had.

On my second day in Hong Kong I managed to contact Ah Sai, and he came to see me in my room. His hair was greying. We didn't hug or kiss. He addressed me respectfully as 'Ah Pah sister' and in his shy way he introduced his wife, who nodded and called me 'Auntie'. She sat docilely in an armchair, after offering me gifts of a box of candies and some oranges.

'Come and meet your Auntie Silver.' Ah Sai beckoned to his adopted daughter.

'Cheng, Auntie has something for you.' I handed her the red-packet of good luck money and a brocade wallet containing a necklace with a heart-shaped jade pendant.

'Thank you, Auntie Silver.' She accepted it shyly with both hands and gave it to her mother for safe-keeping.

'And how is business?' I asked Ah Sai.

'Surviving. We both work, now that Cheng goes to the kindergarten. Only now do I know the importance of saving money for a raining day, with a family I do feel very responsible for their welfare, especially Cheng's education. It's very competitive here in Hong Kong, that's why we work during her school hours, so that we can supervise her while she's doing her homework. I hope she'll have a chance to attend university.'

'You must work hard and not disappoint us, Ah Cheng,'

I said. 'We never had a chance to attend school in our time. You're a very lucky girl.'

Later, I walked to Bonham Road to look for Euston, where I had last accompanied Au Ma and Little Peacock Lien some twenty years before. But Euston was no longer there. The mock castle with the turrets and gargoyles, pillars and pimlicos, has been replaced by high-rise apartments, shopping plazas, a recreation centre: Au Ma had long gone to America to join Little Peacock Lien, whose plastic surgery had been a great success. She had starred in a few American-made Kung Fu movies, and in her spare time she taught Chinese operatic singing and gave lute lessons.

From Kowloon station we boarded a train: swift, sleek, and snake-like, sliding effortlessly through the new territories. We were allocated seats in the train corresponding to the numbers on our tickets. No scrambling, pushing and fighting.

We holders of foreign passports were given soft seats with cushioned backs. The locals travelled on hard seats. A class distinction. When we reached Shenzhen, the train stopped briefly; the crew changed, guards and stewards appeared, wearing masks to serve cups of hot Chinese tea for a copper per cup, and topping spittoons with disinfectant at frequent intervals. Loudspeakers blared the words of Mao, interspersed with military music, and after the stop at Lo Wun, we had to clear our luggage at Customs. This took almost four hours. Each of us was ushered into a cubicle, and in a duplicated form all our valuables such as jewellery, watches and cash were recorded.

Kim says: 'It's well known that Customs in China goes through the new arrivals with a fine-toothed comb.'

'The Sydney Customs fussed over me too, they spilled the whole contents of my suitcases and went through each package when I first arrived here.'

'It's because you didn't declare the Custom form properly, besides Chinese people like to bring in herbs and preserved fruits with seeds, and pork shreds, these are forbidden, for fear of contamination by diseases for the plants and animals here. Australia is isolated from diseases of the other countries.'

'But my neighbour Mrs Chin tells me they're looking for drugs, "white powder", and smuggled gold.'

'They're stricter now, after imposing a ceiling on the amount spent overseas. The Asians used to bring in gold or diamonds to be sold here.'

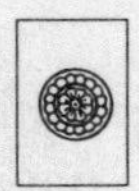

Canton station seemed much bigger and cleaner than the one I remembered. We were met by a guide, whom we addressed as comrade, a middle-aged woman, austere and sober, dressed in a man's shirt and blue pants devoid of make-up or jewellery, not even a watch. She took us to our guest house, the Overseas Chinese Hotel, and bade us goodbye. She promised to be back the next day after lunch. We were given single rooms, the wooden beds covered with a mat and a mosquito net dangled from a frame above. Toilets were communal. Water splashed from the overhead cisterns when flushed, and the taps didn't work most of the time.

Lee Sao came to visit us the very day of our arrival. Bent and shaky, she walked with the aid of a stick. It was the spring of 1959, and she wore a quilted jacket, with many obvious tears and patches, her shoes too were gaping at the toes, she wore a hat made of layers of cardboard stuffing. She lived in Fok Sun with her other nieces and nephews — cousins of Han. She had a meal with us. The restaurant in the hotel was rowdy, people wore shabby clothes, talked loudly and noisily. Tears welled up in Lee Sao's eyes as she swept the rice from the bowl into her mouth.

'I haven't had such pure white polished rice for many years,' she explained with embarrassment. 'It's been so long since . . . I've forgotten what a mushroom tastes like, and even how to bite or swallow it.'

'How is life in China now compared with the old days?' Ah Han asked her.

'Huh,' she sighed. 'Surviving, just . . .' And she looked around her at the large noisy crowd, as if scared to say too much.

'Come up to our room, and we can talk quietly among ourselves,' I suggested.

We helped her up the stairs, and sat her down on a large armchair. Ah Fong offered her a cup of tea poured from the thermos supplied by the guest house.

According to Lee Sao, life in Communist China was spartan and restrictive, but no one starved though only basic food was available on a ration, accorded to work input in the communes or farm. Coupons were issued for cloth — a yard per head per annum. Lee Sao had to save for four years in order to have enough material for a *sam-foo* suit. She was not allowed to buy things from shops — they were only opened for the tourists, the locals weren't even allowed into the Friendship Stores. We showered on her the quilted jackets we had bought in Hong Kong, quilt blankets, second-hand dresses and shoes from Dawn, an automatic watch which Han smuggled in without declaring, light bulbs, batteries, and a transistor radio.

'*Aiyah*, all the old folks of the neighbourhood won't have to wait for their rationed cloth to make their dresses now,' Lee Sao said with delight. 'Their dresses are so tattered and torn, like the beggars' in the old days.'

Early next morning the loudspeaker broadcast words of Chairman Mao followed by military music, urging, 'Forward march . . . forward to victory'.

We joined groups of elderly men and women in the park across the hotel for tai chi, while the young excercised with wooden swords. It was certainly a new and different Canton.

Our guide came after lunch. She told us politely that, as tourists, we were not encouraged to wander out on our own.

'Tell me which scenic places you like to visit and I'll make arrangement. It will take a few days to be approved, authority has to be issued from Beijing. But we have a good programme for you daily. Tomorrow you'll be visiting a silk factory in the morning, a commune in the afternoon and a ballet of the "White Hair Girl" in the evening — it's the story of the revolution against the tyranny of her rich master, and how under the inspiration of Chairman Mao, she gains her dignity in life . . .'

We were driven in an old Datsun, a Japanese car. Along the way I saw piles of metallic objects on the roadside.

'What is that doing there?' I pointed to an old brass four-poster bed outside a house.

'Waiting to be collected by the men in the communes to

smelt down for making of machinery, pumps and tools required for agricultural use.'

'A beautiful bed like that to be smelted . . . what a waste.'

'All that belongs to the bourgeois, the imperialist, capitalist, according to Chairman Mao, this shouldn't be encouraged.'

And we passed hundreds of makeshift brick furnaces in people's backyards, in gardens, corners of filled-in ponds . . . The guide pointed out: 'Here the men will make the tools, while the women work in the farms.'

'What about the children? Who will look after them?'

'The babies and toddlers are kept in creche, all older children go to school, it's compulsory. Men and women have gained equal status.'

We were taken on a tour of the city of Kwangzhou, previously Canton. The Pearl River, Zhu Jiang, the opium dens, gambling houses and brothels now cleared from its waterfront, is a favourite haunt for strollers and lovers at night, who strew the ground with condoms. The young all dressed alike in Mao's blue tunic and pants. Women kept their hair short and straight, and wore no make-up or jewellery.

There were Chairman Mao posters on walls of buildings everywhere. A large portrait of Lenin was hung next to that of Chairman Mao at the front of the Canton railway station. Slogans written in big letters splashed across public places in the city.

'The Great Leap Forward,' Ah Han read.

'What does it mean?' we asked our tour guide.

'It's a campaign which began last winter, launched by our Chairman Mao to mobilise the people to increase industrial and agricultural production through decentralisation.'

'Decentralise?' Ah Han asked. 'What does it mean?'

'It's a three-tier structure — commune-brigade-team. All

farmers in China are organised into some twenty-four thousand communes, each commune is subdivided into a dozen or more brigades, each in charge of a production team, which is made up of the entire inhabitants of at least one village.'

'I would like to visit my village, Lung Sun, to see the production team,' I requested.

'And on the way can we stop at our previous place of work?' Han, Yin and Fong requested to visit Xiao Bei or 'Little North', the suburb where they had worked, and I, the House of Tang in Xi Guan. 'Also on our way back to Canton can we stop at Fok Sun, the Ancestral Temple where we had our "comb-up" ceremony?'

In Lung Sun, I saw my home, now fortified with mud walls, with the wooden plank doors that creaked when thrown wide open to the wind. I saw strangers trampling all over my home, gathered in groups, discussing, reporting on their work and its progress, presided over by a young woman confident in her Mao uniform and cap, and talking with authority. My home was just a shell, filled in by other people from another time, another kind of smell prevailed; of earth, manure and antiseptic. The family Wong Lao and Wong Ma belonged to a past, which only I knew because I had lived in it, shared the sufferings and the giggles of my sisters — real blood sisters. They were all ghosts now, invisible, perhaps they came to haunt this hut at night, their birth place, their birth right.

The guide explained: 'Besides agriculture, commerce and industry are also nationalised, no more private enterprise, everybody works as a collective with pooling of labour and land.'

A furnace stood at the site of the pigsty, which once was my hiding place during the passage of the soldiers in grey uniform; two strangers were smelting scraps, beating the molten metal, making tools, their method improvised, the finished products primitive. I could not locate my parents' graves, those which I had dug with my bare hands, for there was not even a stick to make their burial sites. All empty land was dug up for planting of wheat, the guide said.

The one main street was deserted, all the shops were closed, the warehouse of the previous landlord was occupied by a barefoot doctor. In the rice fields women bent to till and plant, each family in their little plot, as allotted by the State.

The pond where the carp would jump for their food was partially filled in for planting wheat.

I did not want to see any more. I told the guide I wanted to leave straight away.

There was a conspicuous absence of beggars at the Ancestral Temple. It was no longer a place of worship, but treated as a museum of the people's ignorant and blind faith. The inner hall of the temple was defunct. The images of the deities, the eighteen lohans, served as an example for the guide to ridicule the superstitions and belief of old China.

'These gods are made of paper.' And she pushed them to prove her point. 'How can they help you when they are only papier-mache?'

'Where have all the occupants of the Temple gone?' I asked. 'The monks, the nuns, the novices?'

'They're working either in the fields, factories or offices, according to their physique and literacy. They've been re-educated and reformed from leading a life of wastage in superstitious worship and non-productivity.'

And I thought Chairman Mao must be very powerful to be able to reform China from its thousands of years of belief and teaching, to persuade a country to shed its old customs and culture almost overnight.

The charity kitchen now functioned as a creche for children, who dressed in bright coloured frocks, and pink ribbons in their hair greeted us with banners, bidding us *Ah Yee* (Aunties) welcome. The pool was dry, the fountain not working, although the turtle and serpent had survived the tumult of revolution. For a brief moment I was transported back some thirty years in time, when Lee Sao spotted Ah Sai and me sitting here licking our piping hot charity meal.

The House of Tang was a sorry sight. The wall had broken down, the fence of trees and shrubs gone. Each wing was divided into numerous cubicles to accommodate some twenty to thirty people. The courtyards were tilled and used as vegetable gardens where medicinal herbs were grown. No more perfumed gardens, pavilion, or pond with carp, or ivory swing. Even the covered walkways were walled in, used as accommodation.

The only person I recognised was the gatekeeper, his mane of hair now thinned and grey, and he was toothless. His wife's pockmarks now seemed less conspicuous, filled out by the passage of time, she came forward to offer me a cup of tea.

'Our children are serving the country,' she said with pride. 'Our boy is in the army, and the girl a university graduate, an aeronautical engineer.'

I was glad Tai Tai had decided to leave before the revolution, for I would hate to see her struggling with her bound feet in a factory, or the Ancient Mistress lying in a reform camp shivering from the withdrawal symptoms of opium. This way I could preserve their images the way they had always been to me: figures of wealth and aristocracy, swathed in splendour.

On our return to the hotel that night we sisters stayed in Ah Han's room and talked.

'How can we ever return to this new China to retire in our old age? Look at the way they treat the elderly, with no respect. Equality, they say!' Ah Fong aired her doubts.

'And with the ration system, you'll have to grow your own vegetables, and by that time we'll be too old to grow anything.' I didn't particularly like the prospect of tilling the land in my old age.

'I think we'll have to give up that idea, look at poor Lee Sao.'

'I'm most disappointed at the squalor. I thought the Communists had better and more promising plans,' Ah Han said.

'All these years, and now our plan to save and retire here is shattered by what we've seen so far,' a disillusioned Ah Yin remarked.

'We'll continue to work hard and see how China is by the time we actually retire.' Ah Han was the only one who had relatives in China, and deep down she still thought of coming back.

Disappointed and disillusioned, we returned to Singapore after spending three months in China. A whole season.

In Singapore there is no change of season. It's warm throughout the year, except for the monsoons, those heavy downpours which occur two or three times per year. They were noted for overflowing deep drains and flooding streets. But since the new Government installed new giant drainage systems, Bukit Timah Road had never become like a river again.

On my return from China, I started looking for work. Advertisement was by word of mouth. Many of Dawn's friends rang me at Temple Street to help them when their amahs went on leave, and in this way I didn't run short of work. Every few months or weeks I would be working in a different family, filling a temporary job as a *naima*, a cook, a washer and ironing woman. In one family I was solely in charge of her six dogs, for a month. I was rewarded very highly for this special pet-sitting.

'The Great Leap Forward was abandoned, it was a big failure, tools broke down, there were no spare parts, irrigation was a problem, and there was acute shortage of oil as peanut and soya bean planting was replaced by that of wheat . . .'

I heard this news in Cantonese on Chun's radio, two years after our return to Singapore.

'A great catastrophe, starvation is now rampant, with malnutrition and diseases . . .'

I told Ah Yin that since China had become so unstable economically, we might as well abandon the idea of retiring there altogether, and look for some place in Singapore instead.

But at home in Singapore things weren't running smoothly either. There was a rift brewing between Singapore and Malaysia. Television had been introduced in Singapore, and on my days off I would visit Dawn, helping her with house chores and having a chance to watch the six o'clock news in Chinese on her black and white set. I remember the day Dawn summoned me from the kitchen to watch the historical moment when a distraught Lee Kuan Yew appeared in the 'box'. Choked with emotions he announced: 'The merger has ended.' It was the separation of Singapore from Malaysia. With tears rolling down his cheeks he vowed to steer Singapore from British colonialism into a self-sufficient nation: a Republic. Patriotism and pride welled up in me, for Singapore had been my home since my arrival in 1939.

Dawn rang me one day later that year, the month before Christmas: 'Come and stay with us, Ah Silver. Don't take any more jobs, we need you. Wah has picked a day to get married when John returns from Sydney for annual holidays. And Kim has just finished her final examinations.'

I stayed on at Dawn's flat for another two months after Wah's wedding, for Kim had her results and her application to Sydney University to study medicine was accepted. While Dawn went shopping with her, preparing for her overseas trip, I cooked, washed and sewed. Finally, in February 1966, both John and Kim left for Australia. Dawn was all by herself.

Unlike John, Kim wrote home frequently to Dawn or Wah and occasionally sent me postcards.

'*I miss you all . . .*'

'*Feel very lonely, cry myself to sleep . . .*'

She said she couldn't remember much of her previous trip for the heart operation, though the landmarks were starting to make an impression on her.

I would reply promptly to any letter or card that she sent with the help of the letter-writer. The following year seemed to pass slowly, as we eagerly awaited for Kim to come home for the Christmas holiday. She arrived with boxes of cherries and Queensland mangoes.

'John is doing holiday work in the post office in Sydney to earn extra pocket money, as he wants to buy himself a stereo,' she said.

Dawn broke it to her. 'Next year you may have to do holiday job in Sydney too, as I can't afford to pay for your fare to come home every year.'

Wah was expecting her first baby, and Dawn moved into her flat to help her, hence saving on rent and other expenses. An air-conditioner, a luxury item, was installed in the nursery to make the room comfortable and cool for the baby. Wah said: 'Ceiling fans are out of fashion. Most offices and the new shopping complexes are centrally controlled by air-conditioning these days, just like in the cinemas.'

Kam told me about a new campaign starting in China: the Cultural Revolution.

'Lucky you went back earlier,' she said. 'My friend who just returned from China described to me the most frightening experience she had there. The young students, the so-called Red Guards, were given permission to do house search and punish whoever they thought fit. They went on a rampage to destroy the four olds of China: culture, customs, habits, and and religions.'

But in Singapore Lee Kuan Yew too imposed a new regulation. Eng warned me: 'You're not permitted to spit. You will be fined fifty dollars on the spot. Look at the posters with illustrations that say "Don't litter".'

I belonged to the generation where spitting was an accepted habit. To spit out the phlegm, to expectorate, was necessary to get rid of an excreta of the body. Or the thick greenish glob of phlegm would plug and impede intake of air into the lungs.

'*Hak-puh-puia . . . Hak-puh-puia . . .*' was a warning signal that the offensive mucous was about to be spat onto the ground or into a spittoon. Now prohibited. In the name of cleanliness and hygiene, I either had to swallow the phlegm while out in the street or spit into my hankie or the fashionable disposable paper tissue.

Wah gave birth to a boy when her daughter was two years old. Her family completed; as indicated by the poster of the Family Planning Association, showing a family of four: father, mother, daughter and son, with a slogan 'Two is beautiful'. Wah volunteered for a sterilisation operation. She was rewarded with a certificate which entitled her to more deduction in tax, and guarantee of admission into a good school for her children. She was a participant in the Population Control programme. For Singapore, a small island, was threatened with a shortage of housing unless the population explosion was curbed.

Schooling too became compulsory. Illiteracy was gradually becoming a thing of the past. Then came the prohibition of dialects on radio and TV. Lee Kuan Yew announced that the official Chinese language would be Mandarin, and it also became a compulsory subject in all schools.

So from then on Mandarin was used on radio and TV. I couldn't understand it, it was just like a foreign language to me. I missed my Cantonese programs.

There was a whole new generation out there: healthy, literate, bilingual, with westernised names, wearing western dresses, and eating hot-dogs and hamburgers. Yet inwardly they still clung to their Chinese culture. Education offered them a lifestyle of independence and freedom. Women now worked in offices, factories, restaurants or hotels. Domestic workers were recruited from neighbouring countries like Sri Lanka, Indonesia, the Philippines, or Thailand. They stayed on a two-year contract.

There were no more amahs like me. At first I was very much in demand, the brand of superior servant, her life totally dedicated to domestic service. Then as I got older, and my kind rarer, people went for the young and able. I belonged to a dying breed — a species fast becoming extinct.

So were the itinerant hawkers like the 'tin-tin' man, who used to come in the cool of the afternoon, shaking his snake-skin rattle, on his push-cart a trove of goodies, ranging from needles and thread to hair oil and solid face powder. And the knife and scissors sharpener, the cobbler and wooden-clog makers, and all those with their portable woks and earthern pots, selling delicious home-cooked food.

Gone too was the free motor boat from the Keppel Harbour, which used to transport us on Saturday afternoons to a football match on the island of Blakan Mati. Now the island is a resort for tourists: the Sentosa. Ahmed, the driver would rush us to watch the sunset at Mt Faber, then a deserted summit surrounded by bush. And we saw at dusk flickering lights like fireflies wafting towards Singapore shoreline. 'See the satay hawkers with their oil-lamps, they come from the outlying islands in their sam-pans, to set up stalls in Singapore night market.' Ahmed would race the old Humber Hawk down the winding Buena Vista Road, the 'nine curves and thirteen bends', to Beach Road where we savoured freshly grilled satays from the roadside stalls in the open-air *pasah-malam* next to the Alhambra Cinema, within walking distance of Raffles Hotel.

I stayed at my coolie's cubicle, not really keen to start full-time employment, just resting and filling in odd jobs for my sisters and our friends. One day the postman called. Eng shouted from the bottom of the steep staircase: 'There's an airmail letter with wriggly writing for you.' I guessed it was from Kim, and urgent too, for mail was usually sent by sea.

'I'm taking it to the *siasin-loa* to read,' I told Eng, as I grabbed the airmail envelope, edged with slanting red, white and blue stripes, with stamps of the Queen's profile. The midday crowd had dispersed in the market of Temple

Street, and the evening stalls were moving in, their trestle tables heaped with plastic toys, transistor radios, and tape recorders.

There weren't many of them left — these *siasin-loas*, who now charged a dollar for reading and writing a letter. I found him dozing on his stool, leaning against a pillar. A large blue fly buzzed around his nose. He waved his hands vaguely, dropping his newspapers from his lap. His eyelids twitched.

'*Siasin-loa*,' I called. Startled, he woke up, rubbed his eyes, and retrieved his newspapers from the ground. '*Siasin-loa*, I'm sorry to disturb your nap, but please help me read this letter.'

'Sit down.' And he pulled a pink formica stool from under his small foldaway table, cluttered with his paraphernalia for writing: a fountain pen, a bottle of Quink ink, a Chinese inkwell and an ink-stick, writing paper, envelopes, and a hardcover book for paper weight. He prised open my letter with a knife, put on his glasses and remarked: 'It's all in English. I'll scan through first and then read aloud in Cantonese to you.'

It seemed eternity, the time he took to translate line by line the three pages of wriggly writing, scribbling in pencil here and there, pausing to refer to his thick dictionary with dog-eared pages. Finally he peered through his glasses, his gold teeth gleaming as he said: 'It's bad news.'

'Something serious? An accident?'

'Listen,' he began. 'She asks you not to be upset by the news.' He paused.

I clenched my fists. 'Please continue.'

'She is pregnant and unmarried, expected confinement in six weeks' time.' He counted on his calender. 'End of the eighth moon. She says the father of the baby left her when she was seven months pregnant. You're the only person she can rely on to help her look after the baby when she resumes work. She has no relatives there as her brother John has already left Sydney for good, and her mother will disown her if she returns to Singapore with a child out of wedlock . . .'

I knew Kim was right. As an unmarried mother she would make Dawn lose face and be a terrible disgrace to the family, and she too would be ostracised by the prevailing Chinese society.

'She says she has determined to bring the baby up in Australia where there is no social stigma attached to single mothers.' And he peered above his glasses at me. 'Can you make arrangements to go to Sydney in time for her confinement?'

'I must fly there to help her, my little blue baby.'

'Do you wish me to reply her?'

'Yes, tell her not to do anything silly, tell her I'll come as soon as I can . . .'

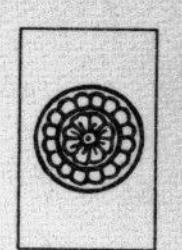

Australia

IT TOOK ME THREE DAYS to obtain a passport and another twenty-four hours to get a tourist visa from the Australian High Commissioner. I withdrew ten thousand dollars from the post office savings account and Wah helped me to book and pay for a flight to Sydney. I bought a bank draft and changed some cash into Australian money — my ten thousand Singapore dollars dwindled to only three thousand and five hundred Australian dollars.

'The foreign exchange rate is roughly three to one,' Wah explained.

'How long do you think three thousand dollars will last me?'

'Depends what you buy, but always think in terms of Singapore dollars, compare the prices before you commit yourself, remember it's three to one.'

I wasn't sure about Kim's financial situation. Kim never used to save money, she would spend whatever pocket money her mother gave her.

'Young people these days have no idea how hard it is for

money to come by, they just buy anything that looks cute and is trendy,' Dawn grumbled.

'*Aiyah*, not so long ago you were like that too, remember you would haunt John Little, Whiteaways and Robinson in the old days just after your marriage, to buy cute things for your babies even before they were born . . .'

'Those were the days when Baba and Nonya Lim were wealthy. Do you know Peng never gave me any of his salary for housekeeping even after we moved out here into our own flat.'

'A parasite, sponging on your money.'

'I was drawing on my special savings, my dowry, from Baba and Nonya, my uncles and aunties, and the good luck money from my wedding gifts. After Peng left, before Baba Lim's legacy came through, I had to pawn much of my gold jewellery.'

'All these years you've been pawning jewellery?'

'Gold is an asset, better than jade or pearl or diamond. It has a universal value. But it must be pure gold.'

I packed my two gold chains, my jade earrings and the large jade ring. I was prepared for the days of adversity, if I had to pawn my portable assets, in a foreign country. I would sacrifice anything for Kim, my once blue baby.

I was scheduled to depart in a week. I made many trips to the tailor, was measured and fitted for Western-style trousers and 'Hawaiian shirts.' I bought a handbag with multiple compartments, two suitcases and Chinese medicinal products — herbs for brewing soup for Kim. I also packed the recipe for lactation given to me by the chef of the House of Tang.

Ah Han, who had lived in Sydney during the Japanese occupation of Singapore, briefed me on this foreign place.

'It's a modern city where women wave their hair . . . there

are cold seasons, so you need good woollen underwear, cardigans, and thick socks and leather shoes. There's a Chinatown in Dixon and Campbell Street where you can buy Chinese dried provisions, and eat in Chinese restaurants.'

Everybody was helpful. My sisters Ah Han and Ah Fong took leave from their bosses and came to Singapore to help me prepare for my trip. Wah chose some baby clothes for Kim, and my friends gave me red-packets of good luck money.

Dawn slipped me a red-packet for safe journey. 'Take good care of yourself,' she told me. She made no reference to Kim.

For the first time in my life I had my hair styled at the hairdressing salon. I wanted to wave my hair like the women in Sydney, to blend in with their style, so as not to embarrass Kim by looking strange or out-of-place with a long pigtail. A big sacrifice. For me, cutting my hair short was like chopping off a part of my body. My hair was an extension of myself, mark of my status. I'd been growing it for the past forty odd years, and now it reached almost to my knees. I used to spend at least half an hour everyday combing it, straightening and smoothing with a sticky lacquer made from shavings of tree bark, plaiting it evenly and loosely from the nape of my neck, trying the end with a black silk braid. My pride, my glory, was this pigtail that dangled low down my back. Shampooing was done once a month, on an auspicious day chosen from the almanac. All the amahs would wash their hair on that day in their individual homes, using natural herbs that kept the hair shiny, smooth and odourless.

'I want to shorten my plait,' I told the hairdresser.

'How short?' She stared at my ugly image in the wall mirror.

'About half the length.'

'What a pity,' she said. 'Such lovely long hair. How many years have you grown it?'

'Nearly all my life . . .' Since the time my head had been shaved in the House of Tang, I'd never cut it.

'Hair will always grow again,' I consoled myself, just as Ho Ma, or was it Tang Ma, had told me, when I resisted vehemently at the House of Tang on the day of my arrival. Hair had always been an asset to me. I had sold it for silver through Lee Sao in my village during the draught and famine.

'Please make big waves — not too curly and fizzy. Cut off the queue in one snip. I want it back for keepsake,' I repeated my request.

I had followed Little Peacock Lien to many beauty salons but techniques had changed since then. Instead of metal clips connected to electric wires, there was strong smelling ammonia, colourless chemical solutions, and plastic curlers.

My friends and sisters remarked that I looked ten years younger with the new hairstyle. My hair rippled in big waves brushed back from my forehead, and plaited loosely into a much shorter queue at the back. I posed for my passport photo, wearing a floral shirt, with one eyelid wide open, the other slightly drooped, smiling into the camera: the image of a modern amah.

I waved goodbye to a small crowd of my three sisters, my friends, Wah and Dawn who had gathered outside the glass door of the Kallang Airport.

A door closed, another opened. A thick secure steel door of the modern 'flying machine'. A hostess counted the number of passengers. I felt proud to be amongst them. To be transported in the 'empty air' in the comfort of a soft cushioned seat, harnessed and secured in place, was something I had never dreamed I would do.

And I plunged headlong, unaccompanied, into a whole new continent. Faraway Australia, foreign Sydney. A city I had so far only seen through coloured postcards which unfold like a concertina. This was where Kim now lived, alone and pregnant, crying out for help.

I was sorry to leave Singapore, Dawn and Wah, my sisters and our friends. Singapore had been my home for thirty-two years; I'd lived here through war and peace, experienced the changes as it moved from a colony to an independent republic. I felt like a caterpillar moulting, shedding my past, and stepping out of my shell into another life. With sadness I gazed down at Singapore from the air, with a bird's eye view of distorted and diminutive houses, skyscrapers looking squat and flattened, streets linear as though drawn by a ruler, the green of stunted trees and lawns, the blue of ocean and sky, and the brown and green blotches of outlying islands with their miniature *kelongs* (fishing station) and then all of a sudden everything was obscured by a blanket of white fluffy clouds like cottonwool.

The stewards and hostesses stood at the front ends of the aisle and began a mime, wearing plastic jackets, pretending to blow a whistle, puffing into a plastic mask, gesticulating here and there, with a background announcement in English. I thought they were entertaining us, to cheer us, the sad ones, who had just said goodbye to those we loved. But my neighbour explained that it was a demonstration for an emergency landing. And it frightened me to realise that we were airborne, lifted high above the earth, no firm ground to step on. Air: a nothingness, impossible to cling to, not even a straw to clutch. I remembered seeing television news of a plane crash — horrific scenes of crushed metal and twisted cockpit, the wreck of a plane burning and exploding . . .

And I inwardly prayed to my goddess of mercy, Kuan Yin, with whom I had taken the vow of celibacy, to whom Tai Tai had prayed and had been granted Ming Ming to propogate the House of Tang. The only time She had failed me was when I prayed for Dawn and Peng to live and grow old together 'till their hair turns silver' . . .

Who was it that told me Kuan Yin was a transvestite? Was it the storyteller in the village? I couldn't be sure. Did it matter what sex She really was, as long as your prayers were answered? Like MeiLan Fong the prima donna of the opera, a male dressed in woman's costumes and singing in a high screechy voice, yet his performance was excellent, no comparison possible. There was a rumour once, not so long ago, that someone had taken a photograph from the aeroplane window, and when the picture was developed and printed, there was Kuan Yin standing on clouds. Chun told me it had happened to a Thai, and the picture had been enlarged and was exhibited permanently in a temple in Bangkok. Large crowds queued up to pray to the photo image, donating money towards the upkeep of the temple. I wondered if Kuan Yin was out there protecting our plane, and I promised myself that I would donate a substantial sum to that particular temple in Bangkok if I should land safely again on firm ground.

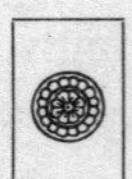

'On terra firma — the firm ground,' says Kim. 'The incidence of car accidents is much higher than aeroplane accidents, riskier travelling on the ground than up there, in spite of the traffic lights and code.'

Whenever I mention the aerial photograph of Kuan Yin, Kim dismisses it with cynicism.

'Just a gimmick, a camera trick to con people who are superstitious. Buddhism is now very popular in Sydney, with the large influx of Asians. The Buddhist monks are buying up land to build their temples or monasteries, there's a large one in Cabramatta, and the main quarters in Wollongong.'

'I've been there on an ACCA outing,' I tell her. 'We were given vegetarian meal. But over the years my enthusiasm and belief somehow has become blunted. The teaching is good, to give alms to the poor, to do good deeds, not to kill and so on, but the promise of becoming a saint in the life after death seems rather far-fetched to me now.'

Drinks and food were served in our individual seats on a fold-away table. My neighbour — a Chinese Malaysian student attending the 'big school' in Melbourne — explained to the hostess that I didn't eat beef and had 'no English'.

The cabin lights were dimmed, I dozed off reclining on the seat, dimly aware of the hostess who gently covered me with a blanket. An announcement in English woke me. Breakfast was brought in a neat plastic tray. My neighbour helped me fill in the immigration form.

'We'll be landing in about two hours' time and there is a time change — Sydney is two hours ahead of Singapore time,' he said.

He showed me the way to the toilet which was half-way down the aisle. There was a queue outside. 'Turn the handle inside to lock and the light will come on automatically.'

It was a very compact toilet, self-contained, with a small wash-basin with hot water tap, and mirror. I'm used to the squatting type, so I perched on top of the toilet seat, and had great difficulty in controlling the stream of urine. I made a puddle on the floor and couldn't find anything suitable to mop up. I pointed this out to the hostess who burst into tears on seeing the mess. The passengers outside didn't look very pleased when I emerged. They were all foreigners. As I was unable to apologise in English, I simply smiled, nodded, and looked remorseful.

The plane tilted. Warm air rushed through the overhead vents. Another announcement in English. My neighbour advised: 'Put on your seatbelt, we're landing soon.'

Outside the window, there was a red glow, displacing the grey of the night. The plane dived, below was a patchwork of colours: green lawns, red brick houses with red tiled roofs, and postage-stamps of blue.

'What are the little blue squares?'

'Swimming pools in the backyards . . .' the student answered.

'Swimming pools,' I echoed. 'Each house has its own pool!'

In Singapore, Wah and John used to go for swimming lessons in the Singapore Swimming Club in Katong, and many people swam in that large pool, with one deep end for diving and a shallow end for children. Others would just swim in the sea in Changi or Ponggol. It was ages ago since I had swum, and I had never had lessons, just kept myself afloat by instinct or dog-paddling in that stream where I washed the clothes and dived for pebbles. I looked out of the window again but the view was obscured by white passing clouds, and I half expected to see Kuan Yin walking on them, but the plane sped on, and the scenery changed: frothy white sea with cliffs, indentations of coastline, and on the horizon a bridge, crescent shaped, spanning a harbour with yachts and hydrofoils, and on the foreshore amidst cranes, machinery and heaps of concrete and sand was a cluster of half-opened gigantic white seashells.

'It's the Sydney Opera House, it will be completed and opened next year,' the hostess informed my neighbour, who duly translated for me in Cantonese.

'So this is Sydney,' I muttered to myself, fascinated by the beautiful harbour. I fell in love with the city right away; a sparkling jewel, more scenic than the estuary of the Zhu Jiang, the Victoria Harbour of Hong Kong, or the Singapore Harbour.

Kim was at the airport to meet me. She was so happy to see me, she hugged and pecked me on my cheeks, just as she used to do when she was young. Her stomach protruded miles out.

'*Aiyah*, so big, it's not twins?'

She giggled, just like her mother. Kim was a replica of Dawn, a younger version, as Dawn had been in the prewar days, round plump face, big black eyes, thick luscious eyelashes.

Kim lived in a flat in Potts Point; an old block without a lift, four storey high. From the sunroom we had views of the uncompleted Opera House, the glistening harbour with its bridge, and toothy Luna Park on the northern foreshore. There were only two large rooms. We slept in one room, and used the other for watching television. The glassed-in sunroom was the dining area, and at one end was a kitchenette, at the opposite end, the bathroom.

In this block of flats we were the only Chinese. All the other occupants were elderly people, single, all Australians. There were more women than men. I met them on the stairs, the women with their wrinkled faces, their painted red lips, and curly silvery hair. They clutched their shopping bags with trembling hands and I could smell their pepperminted breath when they wished Kim 'Good-day'. That unmistakeable minty smell reminiscent of the drunken Master in the House of Tang.

Kim showed me the way to the grocery stores, the supermarket, the butcher, the bakery and the fruit shop along Macleay Street in Kings Cross.

'Point to the goods you want to buy, and show them your money, let them take what is due to them,' she said.

'But how can I leave it to them?'

'The people here are very honest, they don't cheat you.'

'But how do I know how much the goods cost?'

'Prices of items like bread and milk are the same everywhere, there's no bargaining here, so it doesn't matter if you can't speak English, the prices are on display clearly marked in kilos. But no touching, they don't like you handling their goods, it's not like the Temple Street market where they let you pick and choose.'

In the supermarket or even at the butcher, there was not a single live stock visible, no flapping fowl or jumping fish. Everything was dead. Frozen, refrigerated. Chickens, plucked, gutted, cleaned and cut into pieces, were packed and covered in cellophane.

'Where are the heads? What did they do with the entrails, the feet?'

'I'm not sure,' Kim said. 'But the Australians don't eat them, don't like the look of them.'

'Look at the fish, minus its head and tail, already scaled

and filleted. Translucent boneless slices, probably frozen and thawed. People in Asia wouldn't want to buy them, they only pick the liveliest and freshest fish.' And I added: 'They regard such pre-packaged meat as tasteless and inferior. I suppose here I have no other choice.'

'You can't be too fussy here,' Kim said, smiling at me.

Exactly two weeks after my arrival Kim went into labour. An ambulance rushed us to a nearby hospital — the Royal Women's Hospital at Paddington. She was pushed in a wheelchair, while I followed, carrying her bag.

'Come into the labour ward,' she begged. 'I need you by my side.'

I was embarrassed and timid.

'You mustn't let me go through this alone, you're my *naima*, stay with me . . .'

'All right,' I reluctantly agreed. 'I didn't think they let people inside, your father Peng wasn't allowed in, he was left pacing the corridor waiting for Wah to be born.'

'It's different now, they allow close relatives to stay, you're like a mother to me . . . closer, better than my own mother.'

When my mother gave birth behind the bamboo partition, she was left on her own with a basin of hot water, a blade of grass for cutting the umbilical cord, a string for tying it. Her pains and suffering were very personal and private. We would wait outside the partition, until the baby cried — or was smothered — and then only the two elder sisters would go in to help her wrap the baby and clear the mess. We saved the afterbirth to extract its medicinal ingredients for her to drink.

But Kim's labour was the focus of attention in the labour

ward; a topic of concern and discussion among the doctors, nurses and midwives in attendance.

Dripped and drained, every so often she was checked, charted and monitored. She had wires hooked up into machines from a belt around her tummy, recording graphic tracings of her contractions and the heart rate of the baby. Another gadget measured Kim's pulse rate and blood pressure.

I stayed beside her. I whispered: 'You'll be all right, it'll all be over very soon.'

I mopped beads of sweat off her brow, dabbed her dry parched lips with a wet face towel, gave her sips of iced water through a straw. She gripped my hand for moral support. The pains recurred at regular intervals, getting stronger and lasting longer.

'Now push . . . push down . . . as though you're constipated, take another breath and push hard.' The medical student spoke in Cantonese, for my benefit as well.

Kim writhed in agony. Inhaled deeply. Breathed through a face mask. She was encouraged to push, to strain. As time wore on, distressed and exhausted, she begged for a quick operation. She bled, urinated, defecated and vomited all at once.

Suddenly she let out a loud and heart-piercing shriek.

'*Aihaa-yaa-yaa-yaa-yaa* . . .'

Beyond her control, she bore down. Blood and water gushed afresh, and with a ripping tear the baby's head was crowned.

Total chaos. People walked in and out of the labour ward, scrubbed at the sink, dragged trolleys draped in green. Figures gowned in green, capped, masked and gloved, gathered at the foot of the bed: a young doctor supervised by his seniors; pupil midwife directed by a qualified sister, medical students jostled for a view, an anaesthetist poised with a syringe for a pain relief injection, the baby doctor with another nurse stood at a work table top, ready to receive the baby.

Team work for a normal birth.

The baby was finally extracted from the mess of torn tissues, held by her feet upside down, her nostrils and mouth sucked out with a tube.

'Would you like to cut the cord?' The medical student handed me the scissors. 'You're her relative? Mother?'

'Me?' I hesitated, then I took the scissors from her and she directed me the spot to cut, just beyond where she had placed the plastic clip.

The baby was separated from Kim, the cord severed by me.

Almost immediately she cried, a slimy being coated in blood, vernix and meconium, she was handed over to the baby doctor.

Another doctor sat on a stool, and under a bright angle-poise lamp he began the repair job while Kim's legs were strung on stirrups, I shuddered at the inelegant position, I thought: I'm glad I'm a 'comb-up' and have not had to endure such undignified childbirth procedure. At that traumatic moment I suddenly felt a closeness to my poor dead mother, and much indebted to her for giving me life at such terrible expense of pain and suffering.

'It's a girl, a "thousand pieces of gold",' I said to Kim. In the old China, girls were referred to as a thousand pieces of gold. Boys were priceless, their value far beyond estimation.

She shook her head sadly and confessed: 'He'd hoped for a boy. A boy would be a duplicate of himself and might woo him back to me. A girl is but an extension of me so there's no hope of his return. He already has a daughter in Kuala Lumpur.'

'We'll bring up the baby ourselves, between the two of us, eh?' I was thinking of my savings and the meagre gold jewellery. 'We'll feed and dress her adequately, and give her a good education. Daughter makes good companion for the mother, better than a son.'

Kim gave me a weak smile, she looked exhausted.

Kim named the baby Suchin — Purity.

'It's a beautiful name for a girl, so meaningful and easy to call,' I said.

After resting for a month, Kim started doing a casual job as an after-hours or radio-doctor. The pay was double on weekends and holidays.

I stayed home to mind the baby, a job I had been doing since Wah was born in 1940. But with Kim's baby Suchin, some thirty years later, I felt more akin, like looking after a grandchild, and all by myself without the interference of Dawn. I sang the old Malay lullaby that Nonya Lim had taught me: '*Sayan, nono sayan, anak anak sayan* . . .' (love, nanny loves baby). The flat at Potts Point was peaceful, the elderly occupants were quiet, and kept to themselves. I sat in the sunroom with big sliding glass windows, feeding Suchin, and watched the seagulls sweep over the Woolloomooloo finger-wharf, and beyond that the Harbour Bridge and the luxury liners that moored there.

'Million dollar view,' Kim would say every morning when she woke up to greet it.

'It's free, isn't it, to gaze out?'

'Yeah, but if you buy a house or flat with such a view, it'll cost a fortune.'

'Water symbolises wealth. The Chinese love to have a water view too. The *feng shui* of the siting of a home is very important, it influences the wellbeing of the occupants.'

'There goes your superstition. Is this flat a good *feng shui*?'

I spoke loudly and authoritatively, having gained a little knowledge over the years, from Uncle Fatty Lee, Au Ma, Tang Ma . . .

'The axis of the entrance should be in the north-south, and the rooms should be bright and airy, not dark and dingy, and you should feel comfortable when you first enter. And never live in a house where there has been deaths from unnatural causes. That was the purpose of the death houses in the Bullock-cart-water district in Singapore, meant for those who took a long time dying.'

'Well, even I know such houses would be haunted. Ha.'

'Singapore is quite flat, hence it isn't possible for those further inland to have a sea view, but Hong Kong is hilly, most flats have a view. You get used to it and after a while you don't even notice until your visitor points out to you.'

It was the beginning of November, the start of summer, the hot season. Kim had warned me: 'The seasons here are opposite to that in the Northern Hemisphere like China or Hong Kong, where people are now enjoying the cool season, the end of autumn or beginning of winter.'

'So here we're lagging six months behind the Northern what's-its-name?'

'We're in Down Under.'

'Oh. Never call it this name,' I whispered, afraid Suchin might hear or understand. 'Sounds obscene, such a beautiful country with that harbour, don't spoil it by an inappropriate name.'

'Where did you gather such dirty notions from? Thought you were a "comb-up" and celibate, virgin, purity and all that . . . Heh, I read somewhere that some sisterhoods in nunneries are lesbians.'

'Yes, I've heard of them too, referred to as "grinding the tofu", but not us sisters, we're straight and proper,' I assured Kim.

My chores were pretty routine. First thing in the morning I prepared Suchin's feed by mixing the appropriate amount of milk powder with the right quantity of water. The formula had the same label as that sweetened condensed milk which Wah and John were fed on — two birds resting on their nest.

Kim said: 'Such condensed milk is no longer given to babies here, its sugar content is too high and is bad for the babies health, makes them too fat.'

'Fat is a good sign, indicative of growth. Fat means prosperity.'

'People don't want to be fat now, too much cholesterol causes heart attack, even in babies.'

In Lung Sun and Fok Sun, and in Singapore during the Japanese occupation, the beggars were the skinny ones, starving and seeking alms from those who were fat and well-fed. Now thin was beautiful. There was no war and everyone enjoyed peace, and yet they rationed themselves in their food intake, to lean meat, skinless chicken, and salad without dressing, for fear of high cholesterol.

I made enough formula to fill six bottles to be stored in the fridge, and at feeding time all I needed to do was to warm the bottle up. Housekeeping a one bedroom flat was fairly light work too. The floor was carpeted, except for the kitchen and bathroom which was lined with linoleum. I learned to use a vacuum cleaner. No more dusting with feather dusters or sweeping with reed brooms, Kim wouldn't permit it.

'Too much agitation of dust particles in the air, causes allergy.'

I remembered Little Peacock Lien telling me that she had to use her perfume sparingly because Mr Xi was allergic to it, and would sneeze.

I said: 'I thought one would only get allergy with perfume.'

'To almost anything that you're sensitive to,' Kim said.

Kim took us shopping at David Jones. It was Suchin's first outing, and although we carried a foldaway pram and a bag which contained her feeds, nappies, powder, soft baby towel, still I preferred to carry her in my arms, and let Kim push the pram. We stepped on to a long walkway, we didn't have to move, the walkway simply rolled on under our feet, propelling us forward until we reached the end and then we climbed a few steps emerging into a park.

'It's Hyde Park, shield Suchin from the water sprays of the fountain,' Kim told me. 'There, that's the department store David Jones.' She pointed to a large store with glass windows.

I tried to say it. 'Taa-it Ongsee.'

'For goodness sake, say it properly.'

I couldn't get it right, especially the 'v' and the 'j' and the 's'. From then on I referred to David Jones as 'black and white' because of the logo on its packaging; the large black and white hounds-tooth checks.

'Christmas is only three weeks away,' Kim said.

The huge glass windows were well lighted and decorated with nativity scenes: dolls, toy animals that moved, fake snow that fell now and then in fits of sprays, angels which blew their horns at intervals.

'Look, Suchin, look at the baby Jesus asleep in the manger . . .' But Suchin was fast asleep herself in my arms.

The ground floor was a humid jungle of colour and scent.

Jars of lotions, bottles of cream, tubes of make-up, coloured cakes of eyeshadows, rouge in little containers, lipsticks, heavy scent of perfumes hung thick in the air.

We climbed automatic stairs: 'Stand still, and when you reach the last rung step off. Be careful now. Oh, let me carry Suchin, you take the pram.'

I was the country bumpkin again in this modern city. Before I left Singapore I hadn't seen such automatic stairs or automatic walkway, or dolls and animals which could nod their heads in shop windows . . .

Our destination was the fourth floor, a palace of toys and playthings for children.

'You sit there, while I queue up.' Kim showed me to a chair.

A platform was decorated in red with golden stars and cottonwool for snow stuck on. A stout man with long white beard sat on his throne, dressed in red gown with broad white fur-trim. Mothers with their children lined up to have a photograph taken with him. I'd seen this old man somewhere, his picture, in cards which Kim had received during the past week. This celebrity now appeared in person on his throne. He had a bell and a sack, which he would leave on the floor when he wasn't posing with children.

It was a boy's turn, the toddler just in front of Suchin. When his mother approached the stage with him, he bawled, terrified of this man dressed in red with the long white beard, and had to be pacified by his mother and bribed with a Mars Bar from the old man. 'Click' his photo was taken while he was still dazed.

Suchin's turn next. She was awake, and Kim sat her on the old man's lap. She grabbed and pulled his long white beard.

'Stop it. Oh you naughty girl,' Kim said as she released her grip from his beard. 'Give Santa a smile.'

'Click' and Santa smiled with Suchin dressed in her best frock in his arms.

In the tussel I saw that Santa had a fake beard on, it was strung with elastic bands behind his ears.

That was my first meeting with Santa, fake king of Christmas on a red throne, a favourite for photographs with kids, at a cost of ten dollars — I did a quick calculation. By foreign exchange to Singapore dollars it would be thirty dollars.

'*Aiyah*, very expensive for a colour photograph.'

'It's only once a year,' Kim said. 'It will be a good memento of Suchin's first Christmas.'

We walked back through Hyde Park to our car in the Domain, and that evening when I got home I felt unwell, sneezing, with itchy eyes and streaming nose.

'Hay fever,' Kim said. 'You must be allergic to the pollens from the plants in the park.'

Through the night I coughed and sneezed, with running nose, and used up a whole toilet roll.

'You'll have to get used to the fauna and flora of Australia. Take this pill, it's anti-allergic.'

'I don't believe in pills or western medicine. Too potent for my body system, I would rather tolerate it with my own resistance.'

'Stubborn, you'd rather suffer than take a pill. If this continues it will go down to your chest and you'll get asthma,' Kim stressed. 'Asthma that'll make you wheeze all day and night.'

Ah, I have the very thing for it, I thought to myself. I had brought some dried crocodile meat shreds, the Chinese traditional treatment for lung ailments, sealed in an envelope, which I didn't declare at Customs. When Kim was out, I brewed pork rib soup with a few shreds of crocodile meat. After that treatment, the sniffing and sneezing ceased.

Christmas: all the shops in Sydney were geared up for that big day. Pictures of Santa, sometimes riding in a sleigh with reindeer, smiling benevolently, were plastered on glass windows along with bits of cottonwool to fake snow, there were decorations with gold tinsels and bells, silver stars, and white snowflakes, always a fir tree, and chimneys, and crepe paper in red and green. Christmas in Malaysia was for the church-goers. Ah Han told us how her English boss and the three children would dress in their very best to attend church on Christmas Day, and she, the nanny, had to follow them. Christmas for Dawn and Peng in the good old days meant parties and dancing till late in the early hours of the morning in the ballroom of the Raffles Hotel. Dawn, very tipsy, would tell me she'd lost count of the number of *stengahs* she'd drunk. But there wasn't any Santa in any of the shops in the Bullock-cart-water district of the Chinatown, no fake snow either.

Kim drove us to Martin Place one night. Suchin's eyes lit up on seeing the tree strung with coloured lights and hung with packages, gift-wrapped in brightly patterned paper. On the very peak of the tree was a large silvery star. A band stood in a corner, the musicians dressed in dark uniforms and hats, tuning their instruments; puffing into their trumpets, saxophones, and flutes, the conductor ready with his baton in his hand.

'It's the Salvation Army band,' said Kim.

The women, in the same uniform only with skirts instead of pants, stood in a line. More people gathered around the tree after purchasing a candle each to light, and when the band struck up, the crowd sang along to a tune familiar to me.

'I know this song,' I said. 'Wah and John sang this in their school concert once.'

'It's a carol called "Silent Night".'

And the atmosphere livened up with the tinkling of bells.

'I know this one too. You were given a musical box with a reindeer and when the lid opened the reindeer rotated and this tune came on.'

I sang 'Jingle bells jingle bells' to Suchin who stared with starry eyes at the wonder of Christmas.

But Christmas Day itself seemed to me a big anticlimax after all those weeks of preparation and fuss. All the shops were closed, no traffic on the road, and the streets were devoid of pedestrians. I had been expecting the crowd and rowdiness of a Chinese New Year or Autumn Moon festivities, with masses strolling in their new dresses, with parades or firecrackers . . .

'Where is everybody? How do they celebrate Christmas?'

'It's a very private affair, a family gathering for a traditional dinner of turkey and ham and Christmas pudding. And an exchange of gifts,' Kim explained.

'We too can have a family gathering, and have a turkey and ham dinner. I'll cook it the Chinese way.'

It took a while for me to get used to cooking with an electric stove, though it was so easy and clean, without the flying ashes and dirt. Heat without a fire. A modern phenomenon, electricity, the invisible power. I'd heard that electricity could shock and kill; I wondered if it was like lightning, which strikes your heart if you're bad and wicked. But food cooked with electricity didn't taste as good as that cooked over a leaping tongue of flame. The *wok-chi* (the breath of the wok) was missing, and that was the secret of a good Chinese cuisine.

Kim produced from the pantry a tin of Christmas pudding which I steamed and opened to serve as a dessert. I found a coin in my portion.

'Look, how careless, they dropped their money in there.'

Kim laughed. 'It's not accidental, they have included a couple of coins, says here on the tin,' and she examined it, 'it's a genuine sixpence,' she said. 'They don't circulate such coins any more, since they switched to dollars and cents. Come and I'll show you how the typical Australians spend their Christmas.'

Kim drove us to Bondi Beach. It was a bright sunny day, as hot as Singapore, but the beach was packed with people in their swimming costumes, lying on mats, some wearing sunglasses and reading books, some just baking there, face up, smeared with white globs of cream, only a few were surfing. A few families had set up their charcoal grills and sizzled the meat, the men drank beer out of cans, dripping the gold liquid onto the sand.

'No shame, wearing so scantily in public.'

'It's called a G-string, or bikini,' Kim said. 'Sometimes they even take it off for an even tan.'

'*Aiyah*. Aeren't they afraid of getting sunburnt? Of blisters? They should be under a shade . . .'

In the Chinese concept of beauty, dark is ugly. The maiden is always judged by her fairness, her snowy white and flawless complexion.

'They purposely want a tan, it gives them a healthy look, not anaemic.'

It seemed to me that western culture differed greatly from the Chinese, their customs, ideas, myths, beliefs. I thought then that it would take me a long time to accustom myself to the habits of this new and foreign land.

While Kim was out working, I watched television a lot, sometimes with Suchin in my arms, though sometimes I would leave her in the playpen, she liked listening to the music and the sound, while playing with her string of plastic toys strung across the top of the pen.

From the television I learned many English words and conversational phrases like 'good morning' and 'goodbye' especially from 'Sesame Street', where I memorised numbers, and learned to count from one to ten, for their method was a repetition over and over again in a most interesting and diverse way. I almost believed in Big Bird and the cookie monster, and I also learned to say 'thank you'.

From watching these programs, I began to see that, for children at least, life was expected to be fun, that nature was there for us to enjoy, to indulge in at our leisure. There had been no such notions in my childhood.

On the television, the teachers in the nursery classes smiled and stepped down to the child's level, without inhibition, they danced, gesticulated, and talked in a way the children would understand. Unlike in the old China, where teachers were respected and regarded as a class far above the students, the learned ones were aloof and arrogant, and the pupils regarded them with fear. The children here skipped, hopped, jumped around their teachers and laughed, happy, without a care in the world. They could even climb and sit on their teachers' laps if they chose to.

I was glad for Suchin, that she would be growing up in such a healthy and friendly environment, attending such fun classes, lavished with love, guidance and care. But I also wanted her to know the Chinese culture, which she inherited by birth, so that she could have the best of both worlds.

And I felt it very much my duty to nurture her in the old Chinese customs and manners, because Kim herself was now immersed in the western way. She had even forgotten how to read and write Chinese, except her own name.

One day Kim took us to the Zoo. We took turns to push the pram for it was an effort going uphill in a corkscrew motion; now and then we paused alongside the pen of some animals. A giraffe poked his long neck into the sky, towering above the neighbouring shrubs. From the top of the hill we looked back over the sparkling waters of the Sydney Harbour, busy with hydrofoils and ferries to and from Manly, the impressive cliff of the Gap with the lighthouse and Watsons Bay.

'This is the Koala enclave.' Kim stopped at an enclosure with a tall tree with silvery bark and branches with abundant leaves.

'The Koala bears, those soft toys Dawn brought back to Singapore after your heart operation.'

'They're hiding, can hardly see them.'

I lifted Suchin up. 'Up there, hugging the trunk,' I said.

'The dear little things, they're asleep.'

'Can we pose for a photograph with one of them in our arms?'

'Not possible here.'

'But I have seen them do so on TV.'

'Ah, that's in Waratah Park, not here at Taronga Zoo.'

I was disappointed for Suchin, I had hoped to capture her in a photograph with a real Koala to send it to her grandmother in Singapore. It would surely endear the baby to her and warm her heart. Dawn had chosen to ignore Kim since she had conceived a child out of wedlock. We plodded on until we arrived at the kangaroos.

'Look at "si-ki-pi" kangaroo,' I talked to little Suchin. 'And the baby in her pocket.'

'The little one is called a joey. I must say you've learned quite a lot from the television.'

'It's been educational in more ways than one,' I told her.

The television commercials showed me the Australian houses. The Federation ones with tin roof and wrap-around veranda, and the A.V. Jenning's of the latest design, the solar heating, and modern equipment.

The television housewife appeared with her loadful of clean clothes and highly recommended the washing powder she was using; she pointed with her sharp red nails at the big box marked OMO. All smiles. Such domestic bliss. Another lady would polish her antique wooden furniture, rub and polish till it shone. But Ajax seemed to be the solution to all the cleaning, scrubbing and polishing problems. I was impressed. I was becoming familiar with the lives of Australians in the suburbs, their lifestyles, and their furniture layout. What they ate for breakfast, for dinner. Always food in packets. Cornflakes in the morning, and for their dinner potatoes, carrots, steak artistically arranged on a plate complimenting their fresh bright colours.

And I even knew what Australians wore — intimately, under their working clothes. Bond for vests, Rio for stubbies, Triumph for bras and knickers.

It made me blush to watch them hug, scantily clad, and how they kissed mouth upon mouth. I thought how unhygienic and what assault of bad breath they must suffer then, as if to pacify me, the toothpaste advertisements came on, all sparkling white teeth and happy smiles.

The television programs took me on visual tours through various parts of Australia, passing through wide expanses of open bushland, with Skippy the kangaroo.

I followed a safari to the centre of the country, stood gaping along with the other travellers at a huge monolith of a rock, red, orange, ochre, the colour of earth mixed with fire in the brightness of the scorching sun. On another day it was the sea, turquoise shade of blue, pure and clear, and I saw through the goggles of the divers and glass bottoms of their tourists' boats, the creatures under the surface: the most unusual corals with ridges and furrows like gigantic walnuts, phosphorescent sheen of brightly coloured fish of deep canary yellow and a navy blue band for a belt across its waist, then a school of fish with wings like butterflies, thin and transparent with coloured veins, flapping beside an enormous turtle, and the colossal clams slowly opening and closing their shells of mouth, big as a pair of gates, enclosing the small swimming fishes within them.

Afterwards, I marvelled at the wonders of this continent, endowed so richly with gifts of Nature, and I felt very lucky and very blessed to be here.

Our landlady lived on the fourth floor in the same block. Once a fortnight, on a Friday, the three of us would visit her to pay our rent. She lived alone with her three cats, a dog and her parrot. She loved to show off her pets to Suchin, especially her parrot which welcomed us with a loud: '*Ni how, ni how. ni how*'. (how are you) The rent was fifty dollars per week, exclusive of electricity.

'It's cheap because it's an old block, considering it has a water view,' Kim said 'In that new block down the road, which has a security door and lift, the rent is two hundred dollars per week though there is a swimming pool on the roof. But no pets allowed.'

'Six hundred dollars Singapore money for a flat per week.

That's more than a year's rental in Temple Street. And no pets allowed. Poor landlady, she must be in her seventies, hasn't she any children?'

Kim shook her head. 'No close relatives here either.'

'I saw her open her pantry, it's stocked with cans of tin food just like the ones they showed on TV.'

'The cats, dog and parrot are her children. She takes them to the vet when they're sick, treats them with tender loving care.'

'I'm amazed at the way they pamper the animals here, lavish tinned food and accessories on them. I watch them on TV. They are objects of affection. Pets, clean and sprite, come running to their masters' call, coiffured and ribboned wearing coloured leather collars. Their food comes in cans, and is presented to them in nice porcelain feeding bowls. Why do they treat animals in this way?'

'When their own kids grow up they leave home and the parents get lonely and keep pets for company, a substitute for their children. Australian kids don't live together with their parents, not like the Chinese where several generations live together.' Kim qualified: 'The old Chinese, I mean.'

'I'm ashamed to say that in my village in China we used to ill-treat the cats and dogs, we threw them out of our home, fed them scraps of stale food. We killed them for food during the famine, or in time of plenty cooked them as an exotic dish.'

'Is it true they still sell dog's meat on the roadside stall in Canton?' Kim asked.

'It's a delicacy. It's supposed to taste fragrant like roasted chestnut. They'll kill the dog right in front of you to prove they're genuine.' But I was still thinking about our landlady.

'How is she going to manage in her old age?' I asked

Kim. 'I mean, who's going to look after her, when she's ill and frail?'

'The State looks after the elderly, give them an old age pension. It's their due, the welfare benefits, for having paid their taxes all their working lives. There's pension for ill-health, single parents, the widowed . . .'

'A very good system,' I said. 'I wish I could stay on here with you two.'

'What about your sisters and your dream of going to retire in China?'

'It was a dream, an impossible dream,' I said with sadness. 'You make plans years ahead, and many years on you find that things have changed, politically, and relationships are slowly eroded away by years of separation and living apart. I'm not that close to Ah Han and Ah Fong, I am more familiar with Ah Yin because she was in Singapore all those years, and we met and talked frequently, at least once a week.'

I remembered a wise saying in Chinese: 'Better to have a close neighbour than a distant relative'.

And in my heart I wanted to say to Kim: 'You are closest to me; I've known you since the day you were born, you were entrusted to my care, I've cared for you like I moulded clay with my hands and fingers, and now the same tie is extended to Suchin. How can I ever bear to part from the pair of you?'

I looked at Suchin in my arms, so contented and innocent, sucking on the bottle, this precious life on whom so much care and concern had already been bestowed. I thought of all the trained and qualified people who had waited to assist her entry into this world.

And I wished that Dawn would shed all the facade of nicety and come here to share the joy and laughter and fun in the company of her granddaughter and her daughter Kim.

Kim had found a day job in a clinic of women doctors who catered for women.

'I work for a group of feminists, we cater for the women patients.'

'An excellent concept,' I remarked. 'Most Asian women would prefer to consult and be examined by a woman doctor. Certain aspects of women's complaints are too embarrassing to discuss with a male.'

'In our clinic we stress prevention, we check their breasts and do Pap smears, discuss contraceptives, and do termination of pregnancies.'

'Terminate pregnancies? Is that legal?'

The words termination or abortion send a shudder through my spine, they remind me of the dark lanes and alley-ways of Hong Kong and Singapore, where women emerged from the backstreet abortionists, doubled up in agonising pain, bleeding, and the resultant infections that could render them sterile for life. I've heard tales of terrible instruments being used: knitting needles, branches and twigs of trees, slippery elms, seaweed tents, herbal concoctions to drink, enemas for purging, emetics for inducing severe retching, all in the hope of expelling the foetus.

'Nowadays it is possible to prevent pregnancy — there's a wide range of contraceptives — but some women just won't take the precaution. They believe in hearsay from their friends and the women's magazines which distort the facts. What a price to pay.'

'What about adoption?' I was thinking of Ah Sai and his adopted daughter Ah Cheng who had brought him and his wife so much satisfaction and pride.

'With termination so easy who wants to carry the baby to

term and give it away for nothing; you're not allowed to sell babies for money here.'

'In China now it's one child per family, and the reproductive age officially must be more than twenty-five years of age,' I said, recalling what our guide in China had told me.

'China needs population control. Right now its population totals more than a billion,' Kim said.

I had no idea of the enormity of a billion, or a million, my concept of counting the Chinese way was by an increase of ten times; after one thousand, the next big number was ten times that, a *wan* or ten thousands. Kim tried to explain by the number of noughts but it exceeded my comprehension of figures.

I acknowledged China and Hong Kong were very populous, terribly crowded, people there jostled for space and accommodation. But here in Australia, with its vast land and the scanty population, it was hard to understand the need for population control. I said: 'In this developed country, in such time of peace and affluence, I can see no reason whatsoever to terminate lives.'

'But things are different now,' Kim said. 'Times have changed. We women can choose our own lifestyle: to have babies or to terminate the pregnancies. Our lives are no longer dictated by men and their rules and regulations.'

We were watching a program on TV where women were waving banners and burning their bras while marching in the street.

'There is a global movement to liberate women,' Kim explained.

'To liberate women from what?' I asked.

'From the role of housewives. From being men's chattels, not to live just to please men only, not to depend on men for a living, that's why they're burning the bras, women just want to be themselves, be independent, able to earn a living, to achieve equal status with men.'

I've always been liberated, I thought to myself. I'm a wage-earner and don't depend on men for a living, don't use make-up or wear glamorous clothes, I've never worn a bra. I wear a cotton vest which I cut and sew myself. We 'comb-up' amahs are the pioneers of liberated women.

Kim gave me a weekly salary of fifty dollars. One fifth of her pay. After foreign exchange — the rate had risen to four to one — I would get about two hundred Singapore dollars per week. A very fat pay indeed. Four times more than the average amah's pay in Singapore. I was still comparing everything here with that in Singapore.

But then as my mother used to say: 'No man stays well for a thousand days. No flower stays fresh a hundred days.'

A letter arrived for me from the Immigration and Customs Department informing me that my visitor's visa for six months had expired. It was time for me to leave; could I report to them of my flight home.

The thought of leaving Suchin, a six month old babe in arms, and Kim, a full-time working mother, upset me terribly. My loyalty and devotion to Kim demanded that I should stay to help them.

'Please can you help to extend it at least until Suchin is bigger and toilet-trained?' I asked Kim.

'Perhaps on medical grounds. If you consult an eye-specialist and receive treatment, perhaps you can extend your stay for a while, six months, three months . . .'

The eye-specialist in Macquarie Street gave me a certificate to extend my stay for a bogus eye operation. He wasn't interested in examining or treating me. Didn't even give me a prescription. His receptionist handed me a bill for sixty dollars.

I paid to obtain a fraudulent excuse to stay on. Temporary. On purchased time. I became rather depressed and frustrated, and my heart was heavy with guilt as I pushed Suchin in her pram daily to a park nearby.

'The one with a round spiky fountain,' I mentioned to Kim.

'It's the Fitzroy Gardens.' Kim looked up the name in the map.

There were always elderly people sitting on benches with their shopping bags full of bottles or cans. Young people lay on the grass exposing themselves to the sun. Passers-by would sometimes come and admire Suchin in her pram. 'Lovely lovely,' they muttered. I felt shy and blacklisted, because of my illegal status.

Whenever I saw a policemen I would hurry away to avoid him. Once a car had to brake, screeching to a halt to let me cross the road. The policeman came towards me. I thought: this is the end of me, I'll be deported. But instead he helped me push the pram across the busy junction at Kings Cross. I thanked him profusely for saving my life. I thought: these *feng kwei lao* aren't so barbarous after all. They have kind hearts and are more civic-minded than the Chinese males, who care only for themselves, and would never stoop to help a female or child.

Six months passed. I was counting the months to when my certificate would expire.

Kim said: 'There's going to be an election, bound to be changes, perhaps an amnesty, then you could apply to stay on.'

I visited the eye-specialist in Macquarie Street once more to obtain another medical certificate for extension of my stay, this time for three months. The fee had increased by five dollars to sixty-five.

'It's Time,' Kim said. 'That's the motto of the election.'

We were deluged with news of the coming election. We watched the candidates on television making speeches, debating, pledging their promises to improve Australia when elected.

I remembered voting in Singapore. 'Vote for the PAP,' everyone advised. I presented my identity card, and had my thumb print taken; on the election day I was shown where to mark an X in the ballot. Lee Kuan Yew was elected, and he had held that position in Singapore for many years.

'He had no opposition. There was no other party elected except the PAP,' Kim said. 'They dominate the whole legislative assembly there. He jailed his opponents without trial, one of them was our neighbour in Scotts Road. That's not fair. It's more democratic here in Australia. There's strong opposition and other parties too can voice their opinion.'

On the television a giant figure, tall and broad, spoke eloquently.

'Listen,' Kim said. 'It's Gough Whitlam. He's offering a new deal for the pensioners, migrants, women, Aborigines and students . . . There is hope for you, Silver Sister. You'll have the opportunity to apply for permanent status if he's elected.'

Before I left Singapore Ah Chun had warned me that there was a White Australia Policy, she'd heard from her cousins, the children of her uncles who had come here as indentured labourers in the gold rush days.

'Chinese are a minority group there, and not allowed to own properties,' Chun had told me. 'I heard from my two cousins when they returned to China to look for wives, they said western women don't make good housewives, too independent and often unfaithful.'

'That must be a very long time ago, surely,' Kim said.

'More than fifty years ago,' I said. 'That was when she first met her cousins in rural China.'

And when Suchin was a year old, in 1972, Australia elected a new Prime Minister, Mr Whitlam.

'He's abolished the White Australia Policy, and has officially recognised the People's Republic of China,' Kim told me.

A giant figure. A pillar of strength and hope for me. I was elated.

In early 1973, my application for Australian citizenship was approved. Kim arranged for me to take the oath of allegiance, I was relieved to find that I was the only one at the ceremony.

Kim acted as my interpreter. The officer nodded. 'Raise your right hand,' Kim said. 'Repeat after him.'

I mumbled whatever he uttered, with some prompting from Kim, not understanding a word of it. I received a certificate of citizenship with the emblem of Australia — a kangaroo and an emu standing amidst branches and leaves — the flora and fauna which I'm no longer allergic to.

I thought of Ah Sai in Canton, who had to learn the thirty-six oaths of his Triad Society by heart; yet it was much easier for him to recite in a dialect he knew well — Cantonese. Ah Sai had been rewarded with a tattoo on his arm. I wondered whether he had got rid of it, now he was no longer a member.

'He would require excision — surgical removal,' Kim said.

'It's only a simple pattern.'

'In which case he won't need a skin graft.'

'It would be much simpler just to wear his sleeves down to cover it.'

'Some Triad members have elaborate pattern on their backs,' Kim said. 'I saw a group at a picnic on Bondi Beach, they all had a huge dragon in many colours, spread over their whole back.'

'That would be hard to excise!' I laughed. I felt happy, light-hearted, and we stopped in a city cafe across from the Immigration Office for a cappuccino. I hadn't felt so jovial and relaxed for a very long time.

Legality restores confidence and security in me; gives me a sense of belonging here. I no longer need to run away from a policeman or feel guilty about earning a salary from Kim. To have permanent residency and to be a citizen of Australia is a wonderful achievement. I am now a free woman and have the whole world before me. Life, whatever is left of it, for I've reached the age of sixty-one in 1973, should no longer be empty or sad, but something to be enjoyed. I must put my past behind me, shut that door of suffering, misfortune and thoughts of death. The idea of going to die and be buried in the ancestral village seems no longer realistic or practical.

'It's Time' becomes my motto too. Time to change my outlook on life, my ideals, and my aspirations. I am a simple person, and my taste is humble. But I do wish to be among friends who are close and dear to me, and to lead a peaceful life, without further upheaval or dislocation.

I decided to improve myself. Kim encouraged me to learn English, and I joined the Australian Chinese Community Association (ACCA) which was housed on the first floor of a shop-house in Dixon Street, accessible by a very steep stairway not unlike that of my coolie's cubicle in Singapore. Besides mailing me a monthly bilingual newsletter, the ACCA also organised social gatherings and outings where we Chinese could meet other members and make new friends.

I enrolled in an ACCA English class for migrants. My classmates were a mixture of young ones, many middle-aged couples, plus a few oldies like me. The women outnumbered the men. We sat at a long table, on three sides, facing the blackboard. Our teacher, Mrs Sung, was a Chinese from Hong Kong. On my right sat Mrs Tran, and on my left Mrs May Ly. We always sat at the same place. They were both from Vietnam, of Chinese descent, and we conversed in Cantonese. Mrs May Ly was in her mid-thirties and had a young family: a boy and a girl. They had come to Australia as 'boat people,' refugees. Her husband was an ex-policeman of Saigon. May came to class dressed in shirts, jeans and sneakers donated by Vincent de Paul.

Mrs Tran was about my age. Her husband had died in a refugee camp in Thailand, but her family of thirty-three members had been united here, having flown from Saigon, via Hong Kong. All such refugees were on social benefits and lived in flats supplied by the Housing Commission.

During the tea-break I listened to their adventures and tales of their escapades from a country of terror. I admired their courage and endurance and their determination to start a new life here.

Mrs Sung did her best to teach us the alphabet, and correct pronunciation. She passed on print-outs, showed slides, illustrations and played video and audio tapes. I was so excited and looked forward to attending the class. I took Suchin, a toddler, with me. To be a student was a privilege which had been denied to peasants like me. In my village of Lung Sun, there was not even a school. Only the rich children were educated, as in the House of Tang in Canton, for only they could afford the hefty fees of a private live-in tutor.

But I was already too old, my mind seemed incapable of retaining or receiving any new knowledge. I often forgot what I had learned the day before. 'In one ear, out the other.'

I found it hard to roll my tongue when saying the 'r' and 's', 'z' and the 'sh'. Even the 'f' hissed through my dentures. Everything was so different here, the opposite, back-to-front. My surname came last and the given names first. And the arrangement of the book and text was the antithesis of what Au Ma had taught me in Hong Kong. When the teacher said open the book she meant look at the last page; and to read you had to go from left to right and not from top to bottom from the right-hand corner. All very confusing. But the worst of all was the grammar: the tenses, genders, nouns, and the plural and singular numbers, for there was no such equivalent in the Chinese language. For the past tense we simply qualified by adding 'yesterday' or 'last month' or whatever date . . . The writing was wriggly, like chicken intestines, consisting of alphabets strung together. I was totally lost. At least the Chinese word or ideogram, which consisted of strokes, often gave the clue to the meaning of the words.

At the end of term I was reimbursed three hundred and twenty dollars, as a migrant, to learn English. Kim told me that it was the new Prime Minister — the Giant — who made it possible. How generous of the Government!

And by the end of the three months' intensive course,

although I couldn't speak English, I'd become great friends with Mrs Ly and Mrs Tran, and we exchanged addresses and telephone numbers, and promised to keep in touch.

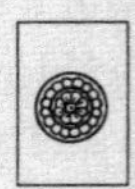

In everyone's life there are moments when the contents of a letter unexpectedly turn a dream into a nightmare, or trigger off an unlikely journey, or even spring open a door usually locked. A voice conveys through the jumble of words a sea of dizzy emotions, torments of the soul, anguish of the mind. We are filled with compassion and sympathy, and succumb to the imploring pleas.

Kim received a letter from Wah. 'Come home as soon as possible, mother has suffered a stroke, she's very ill, paralysed from the hip, and her speech is slurred. Last night she tried to call you, I heard her sputtering something like K-k-mm-m-m.'

A second letter followed: 'There's complication, the doctor found a fibroid, and she's bleeding from down below.'

'We must go to visit her, after all she is your mother, and she may be dying,' I told Kim.

And so we flew to Singapore.

We landed in a brand new modern and air-conditioned airport, with stretches of automatic walkways like that in the Domain of Sydney. Piped music accompanied us, and when we descended the escalator there was a tinkling sound of water from a fountain. Pots of exotic orchids of mauve and black and pink were displayed against the wall. Outside on a platform tourists posed for photographs in a trishaw on exhibit.

'Whatever happened to the Kallang Airport?' Kim asked a fellow tourist as we waited in a queue for the Immigration process.

'It's become the National Sport Stadium,' he replied.

Dawn was semi-conscious, and though she couldn't speak she puffed her cheeks to call K-k-mm-m-m, spraying saliva in the attempt. A tear trickled down her cheek as she held Kim's and Suchin's hands firmly in hers.

A week later she passed away and was cremated.

I didn't like the idea of cremation, being burned in a coffin, it had never been a tradition of the Chinese.

'Why couldn't she be buried like Baba Lim?'

'We never had a chance to discuss her preference. Her stroke happened suddenly, so unexpectedly. Besides the Government encourages cremation, due to scarcity of space,' Wah replied.

'It's cleaner this way, and since we all live in different countries — John is in America — we can each take some portion of her ashes with us, and don't have to bother about "sweeping the grave" as is the old Chinese custom,' Kim said.

'Her ashes will be stored in a permanant place in a memorial temple in Yio Chu Kang, with her photograph above the niche,' Wah explained. She promised she would bring flowers on her birthday and other festive seasons.

'You too can pay her a visit whenever you stop over in Singapore, Silver Sister.'

Singapore had undergone a vast cosmetic change. I had

difficulty in recognising the landmarks. The old and dilapidated buildings were gone, replaced by modern multi-storeyed glass and marble complexes. Trishaws were now used to pedal tourists around Chinatown. Modern cars ran along freeways and highways. High-rises stood on the reclaimed land. The Katong Park and the Singapore Swimming Club, once on the waterfront, were now very much inland. The bungalows on stilts along Orchard and Scotts Road had disappeared. In their place there was a row of five-star hotels, air-conditioned shopping arcades with escalators, see-through bubble lifts, theatre-restaurants, discos and fast-food stalls. I was surprised by the number of Japanese-owned department stores.

'How can the Singaporeans forget so soon, so easily, the bitterness of the war and the life and suffering during the Occupation?'

'*Aiyah*, it's so long ago, more than thirty-five years before I was born, and I'm a post-war baby,' Kim said.

After the funeral, I stayed in Temple Street with Ah Yin for a few days to sort my possessions. The street market had been relocated to a new high-rise complex further down the road. My letter-writer, the *siasin-loa*, too had gone. Nobody knew his whereabouts. I couldn't find anyone to read or reply to Ah Han's letters. And I couldn't write to Ah Sai either.

We communicated by telephone instead.

'Ah Fong has been admitted to hospital, the doctor said it's terminal stage of cancer, and her days are numbered. I didn't tell her, or she'll be so upset. Come quickly,' Han said.

I left by train for Seremban in Malaysia with Yin to visit Fong, and Ah Han joined us from Kuala Lumpur. Two weeks later Fong died in our midst. We knew then that we would never return as a foursome to our village to retire as we had planned.

I was devastated by this trip. I had lost two people who had been close and dear to me. And Dawn was younger than myself. I wished she had made up with Kim earlier, and had come to know Suchin under better circumstances. And although I had never really known Ah Fong well, she had been my sister, by solemn vow.

Before I left for Sydney Ah Yin told me: 'I hope to join you in Sydney, I have offer of a job there.'

'I'm so glad you can be with me, at least we'll be together. Tell me how did you get this job?'

It was recommended by her former mistress of Canton: the mandarin's wife, with whom Ah Yin had frequent correspondence through the medium of a *siasin-loa*.

'I'll be working for the family of a rich restauranteur, Mr Wu, in Sydney.'

'He is very well known in the Chinese community, with his public appearances, and is owner of a chain of restaurants — Wu San, Wu Han, Wu Tien — all in Chinatown,' I told her.

Returning to a place where you've lived before, no matter how briefly, gives you a feeling of familiarity. It is as if you have left a part of yourself there, have gone away just to hibernate, and have now come back, more mature and keen to continue where you've left off. To settle down. To grow roots.

On our drive into the city I recalled with fondness and affection the memories of Suchin's birth, Kim's pains, suffering, tolerance and triumph. As our taxi sped along the Southern Cross Highway which straddled a green golf course, the sunlight filtered through the early morning dew. Sunny Sydney. Brilliant city. South Dowling Street seemed much broader without the congestion of the morning peak traffic. The two storeyed terrace houses with iron-lace trimming, so typical of Surry Hill, Darlinghurst, and Paddington were a heart-warming sight. At the confusion of the traffic at the junction of Kings Cross I wound down the cab window. At once I recognised that smell of faint stale beer, fishy putrid semen of discarded condoms, and the vinegery odour of used syringes among the piles of garbage. Those smells and sights were familiar features of my daily stroll to Fitzroy Gardens with Suchin in her pram. The mobile neon signs of the Pink Panther, across the road from the corner with the big wriggly writing of Les Girls, twinkled to welcome us home. And after we passed the ball of fountain with spiky jet-sprays, we were not far from the Chevron Hotel, where bellboys with white gloved hands rushed to open car doors anticipating tips. We were nearly home. Potts Point, with the warm salty sea-breeze. Sydney awake and alive, with cars crawling along the Cahill Expressway. People were leaving for work clutching attache cases or slung with shoulder bags, running to catch buses, hail cabs. We struggled with our heavy suitcases up one floor to our flat with its 'million dollar' view.

'I missed this view every single morning while we were

away,' Kim exclaimed. 'It has been a habit for me to take in the view from the sunroom en route to the kitchenette or toilet.'

'And we've been away four months, did you have to pay rent?'

'The landlady only charged a small nominal fee for keeping the unit for us.'

Only four months, yet during our absence there had been a lot of changes in Sydney. We discovered that the old vegetable market behind Dixon Street had been relocated to Flemington. A weekend bazaar, 'Paddy's market', had taken its place instead in the Hay Street complex. It rather resembled the Temple Street market: stalls on trestles selling vegetables, fruits, baskets and boxes of them spilling onto the ground, with display of prices clearly marked. Vendors shouted their wares. In another section, cartloads of locally made clothes, plastic toys, Australian souvenirs made in China and Korea. Here I could handle the wares, taste and feel them, the vendors would still extoll me to buy.

I learned to say 'Alf a kilo' and hand them the ones I had picked. Local produce such as fruit and vegetables were much cheaper than in Singapore, where most things were imported.

'Singapore has used up its farming land to build factories or high-rise, nowhere to grow their own food,' Kim said.

There were many Chinese selling vegetables, and I became their frequent patron.

'These Chinese vegetable gardeners are probably the descendants from the gold rush days. Probably some relation of Chun . . .'

'There are lots of Italians growing fruits too.'

There were a few stalls selling fish, not live but fresh,

unfrozen or thawed, I picked and chose the better ones, judging by the lustre of sheen in their gills.

The late 1970s saw a large influx of Vietnamese boat people. Kim read the papers, and we watched the television news at six o'clock, they came in rice barges, often overcrowded, whole families and their children. These were reported to have survived raids by pirates. They told of many who had drowned.

There were changes in the Chinese restaurants too, they had become more sophisticated, offering more authentic Chinese food: roast pork buns and bean-curd pudding replacing the chop-suey and 'long and short' soups. Restaurants sought to outdo each other in decor and new dishes. Many Vietnamese, those of Chinese ethnic origins who could speak Cantonese, worked as waitresses in these restaurants.

Kim took me to the outer western suburbs of Sydney.

'Cabramatta has become a Vietnamese town, I hear the groceries there are very cheap. It's close to the refugee centre of Villawood, so when the refugees are released they automatically look for somewhere nearby to start their business.'

It was like another Chinatown, with Vietnamese butchers, bakeries and home-cooking restaurants. The signs were in Chinese and Vietnamese.

'But it's not safe here,' Kim said. 'The radio often reports cases of robberies, even in broad daylight.'

One day I had a call from Yin. A local call. She was in a great hurry: 'I'm in Sydney. Quick, take down this telephone number, phone me only next Tuesday morning about eleven. Have to go now.'

I had to wait a whole week before Tuesday came. I discussed it with Kim.

'Why is she so mysterious? Is she illegal?'

Kim shook her head. 'Not if she works for the Wu, such prominent figures in the community.'

Kim took Suchin and me to one of Yin's boss's restaurants, Wu Han, in Dixon Street. Mr Wu, the owner, in his white suit, fat and greasy with sweat, went from table to table, to greet customers, enquiring if everything was okay. It was a full house. Then he stood with the cashier, supervising the take for the night.

Kim remarked: 'He looks benign. I think Yin is just homesick.'

But a week was a long time to wait. I counted the pages on the large day-a-page Chinese calendar. I was worried for Yin, after her abrupt conversation on the phone, and the restriction to phone her only on Tuesday. So different from the cheerful tone of her last letter written a month before, when she was waiting to fly over here with her new boss and family. Yin was the closest to me of the three sisters. She must be unhappy, I thought.

Tuesday came at last, and exactly at eleven I rang the number.

She answered at once, and spoke very softly. 'I'll meet you tomorrow at the Burlington market — eleven o'clock. Can't talk now. Remember, the Burlington, next to Mr Minit counter. Wait for me if I'm late . . . don't go away. Wait.'

She bought some groceries and I brought her home to Potts Point and cooked her a meal.

She was in a dilemma. Not happy at work, but couldn't resign because she had signed a ten year contract with them.

'Did you understand all that small print in English?'

'There was an interpreter in Chinese. You see, I was keen

to work in Sydney to be near you. And having a guaranteed job with one family meant continuous income so I signed with my right thumb print . . . I've been here only one month, and now I'm regretting it. I can't resign because the contract imposes a penalty rate equivalent to half the total salary I would have received in work.'

'But why are you not happy?'

'I'm treated like an indentured labourer . . .' and she broke down. In between sobs she described in detail how she was exploited. She worked every day of the week from early morning till late at night — washing, scrubbing, cooking, ironing, doing errands, waiting on the mistress and her three grown-up daughters, enduring their complaints and insults.

'Maybe they're just fussy, but look at the money you're saving,' I tried to comfort her.

Yin shook her head. 'I've barely enough money to live on. From my salary they deduct board, electricity, water, phone, gas . . . I pay my own bus fare and pay for my own food. I don't have anyone to talk to, or to help me write a letter to Han in Kuala Lumpur. The only time I can receive calls is on Tuesday when the mistress is at the hairdresser. I'm most unhappy . . .'

'How often do you come out to shop?'

'They allow me the first Wednesday in the month only, for three or four hours.'

'Don't be too upset, I'll discuss with Kim how to solve your contract. At least we can meet once a month, and I'll phone you every Tuesday. You must let me know if they ill-treat you in any way. I'm your sister.'

The Year of the Monkey — 1980 — ushered in a new decade of chaos and unrest; the mischievous Monkey ran amok with his antics and tricks.

On the television news I saw the English Prime Minister, Mrs Thatcher arriving in Beijing. Kim said she was going to negotiate with the Chinese about the expiry of Britain's lease of Hong Kong.

'In seventeen years' time, Hong Kong will revert to China,' Kim explained.

But it seemed Mrs Thatcher didn't get on too well with the Chinese. This sent waves of panic through the people, and Hong Kong was in turmoil.

Reports from Hong Kong showed long queues at the various foreign embassies where people were applying for migration. I approached Mrs May Ly to act as my letter-writer; she wrote to Ah Sai, asking him if he would like to apply to migrate to Australia with his family. I wasn't sure if I could qualify as his sponsor, but I thought it might be worth a try.

Ah Sai replied: 'I and my family still stay in Hong Kong no matter who governs it, for aren't we all Chinese? Besides, I do not have the money, the qualifications or the inclination to migrate.'

He was adopting the same attitude as that Uncle Fatty Lee had expressed. I could never forget the way he had stood with his arms akimbo on the wharf of Canton, with little Ah Sai beside him, when I had set sail on the S.S. *SeaKiang*, so many years before.

Ah Sai wrote: 'Many people I know who have some connection with Australia are coming as tourists with a package tour, with intent to stay on . . .'

'They're the illegal migrants, who dare not surface or

they'll risk deportation, and they would rather stay on here, even knowing they'll be exploited,' Kim said.

'In such a big country, they'll have no trouble hiding,' I said.

'Some apply for driving licenses to use as identity documents, giving false addresses.'

Thefts and burglaries had become commonplace in Sydney. Our money left for the milkman and the newspapers outside our door were stolen. Most of our neighbours' flats were broken into. Pensioners were mugged even in their own stairways. Deadlocks, padlocks, safety chains, burglar alarms, became compulsory. Our neighbours, under the pretext of alcohol, ordered us blatantly: 'Go home, return to your own country.'

Kim said: 'Can't really blame them, because many thieves and bag-snatchers are Asians.'

I wanted to declare to them: this is my country too, I've made Australia my home.

'Their ancestors had been here for many generations, and they consider us newcomers as outsiders, invading their territory,' Kim explained.

'Weren't their ancestors indigenous to this land?'

'The Aborigines were the indigenous people when Captain Cook first came and claimed the land for England. Years later, when the English jails were overcrowded, many convicts were shipped here.'

I remembered that once we had flown down to Hobart for a week. Kim drove us to Port Arthur, where we visited a cottage built by convicts who had left their marks or signature on the bricks; and in the jail I saw the handcuffs, manacles, balls and chains used to keep the convicts in check.

'Were there women convicts or did they only send the men?'

'Yes, I've read there were women convicts too.'

I imagined the convicts mating among themselves to produce a whole nation of Australians.

'But no, not as you imagine, the male and female convicts were kept separate. Later other settlers came, to raise sheep and cattle, and start other industries.'

'And the Chinese came during the gold rush.'

'Other Europeans came after the first and second world wars, lots of Greeks, Jews, Turks, Italians . . .'

'And now the Asians,' I said. 'In every nation or race of people there are good and bad. No exception with the Asians.'

One night, while watching the evening news on television, Kim shouted, 'Silver Sister, come quick, Mr Wu is on the news . . .'

'Mr Frank Wu, a prominent Chinese restaurateur has been found murdered in his home in Coogee, his throat slashed from ear to ear, hands tied together. Mrs Wu and the maid Yinny were also tied, gagged and slashed, but Mrs Wu managed to crawl to the front door to alert the neighbours. Yinny was found unconscious, in a critical condition . . .'

'It's Ah Yin, my sister! Is she going to die?' I was hysterical and shocked. 'I want to visit her. Kim, take me to the hospital.'

Ambulances, police cars, stretchers flashed across the screen. The first stretcher was fully covered with a white blanket. The next two showed drips and oxygen masks and the upper bodies of women with ruffled hair.

'That's Sister Yin,' Suchin pointed to the last stretcher.

'I hope she'll live, poor Yin,' said Kim 'I'm afraid we will not be able to visit her now. The police will want to speak to her. Perhaps in a day or so . . .'

Yin was in intensive care at the Prince Henry Hospital

for two weeks, before she succumbed to a lung infection.

I was not allowed to get close to her bedside while she was in hospital, because of her isolation due to infection, as well as being under police surveillance. My vowed sister Ah Yin, with whom I had hoped to spend many more years in Sydney died without ever gaining consciousness. I lost another sister, my favourite of the four. Now there was only me and Ah Han left, and we were oceans apart. I grieved for weeks, lost my appetite, though I couldn't shed any tears.

A couple of months later, Kim read the results of the coroner's inquest into the case. 'Yin was an innocent victim of a Triad revenge for the exploitation of a waiter in Mr Wu's restaurant,' she told me. Her mistress and her three daughters survived.

I paid May Ly a visit at her Campsie flat. She seemed settled and comfortable. She told me her husband had a job as a clerk in the Immigration department. She helped me to write a letter to Han, telling her of the tragic death of Sister Yin. She also read me a letter from Chun, the sub-landlady from Singapore.

'Temple Street has been spared from demolition. The owner has terminated my lease now that the house has been listed as a Singapore heritage building. I, Eng, Kam and Goh are planning to retire at Shenzhen where we've bought a new apartment. It's conveniently located between Hong Kong and Kwangzhou (previously Canton). Wah has moved your things from the coolie's cubicle and is storing them in her house, so that you can sort them on your next visit to Singapore.'

After the deaths of Dawn, Ah Fong and Ah Yin, I felt very depressed. I became more aware of stiffness, aches and pains in my limbs, my back. I remembered the Ancient Mistress, who had Peony and Peach to hammer and massage her shoulders, and I thought of Lee Sao, hunched and bent with a walking stick, groaning and sighing.

Gradually my eyesight deteriorated. Lines like lightning slashed from the corner of my eyes as I turned my head, and specks of dirt floated in front of me. Words and print became blurred. I mentioned it to Kim, and she at once demanded that I consulted an eye specialist, not that phantom one in Macquarie Street, but a local Chinese graduate to whom I could explain clearly my problem in Cantonese. He sent me to an optician.

I was fitted with a pair of glasses, bifocal, for reading and watching television. This cost me one hundred dollars. But I didn't mind as my salary has increased by five dollars per week every year.

'In keeping with inflation,' Kim said.

Then my stomach played up; I felt a nagging pain. Kim recommended me for an X-ray. It showed collapse of parts of my spine.

'Osteoporosis,' Kim said. 'Your bones are very fragile and thin, and they collapse upon each other.'

'How did it happen?' I was shocked. I had been quite healthy, ate moderately well, and retained the same weight.

'When did your periods stop?'

'I stopped "riding the horsy" a long time ago, in Singapore.'

'*Aiyah*, no wonder your bones are brittle. You're shrinking. Suchin is even taller than you. You need hormone replacement therapy and calcium tablets to protect your skin, bones and heart. Chinese herbs and traditional medicine will not help in this respect,' Kim said.

But even before I began the hormone therapy my 'horsy'

suddenly reappeared — a sticky dark colour with an unpleasant odour. I had been losing weight, hair, and sleep. Even Kim looked worried, she said Chinese medicine could not help you diagnose or treat cancer. Though I was reluctant, she persuaded me to see a lady specialist. I was admitted the following day to a private hospital for a 'clean-out' procedure, under general anaesthesia, just to make sure there was nothing sinister.

Kim assured me that expenses would be paid by the private insurance.

I was starved overnight. The hunger-pangs of the days of famine in Lung Sun returned. Someone stuck a needle into the back of my hand, and I felt the cold liquid coursing up my arm, then suddenly my mind and thoughts were shut off. My last image was the clock in the theatre showing ten o'clock. Everything went blank. Total black-out. A kind of death.

When I woke up, I felt a soreness, a split in my skin, and some spotting down below. Someone had tampered with my insides. I thought 'I'm no longer a virgin'. How ridiculous for this to happen at my age and after my vow of 'comb-up'.

I told Kim: 'In old China the mother of the groom would go and examine the bed-sheet the morning after the wedding to check if there was any sign of bleeding, to prove the virginity of the bride.'

'To remain a virgin till the wedding night is a rarity nowadays. It's archaic,' Kim said. She picked up my pathology report. 'Good news,' she said. 'It's not cancer.' She looked relieved.

Cancer seems to be the fear of the hidden. A new word. Something unheard of in my far-away ancestral village, where people were plagued with abcesses, festering wounds, leprosy, smallpox, and the chronic killer 'consumption'.

Old age was inevitable, and crept on steadily; the first telltale signs were my hair. I applied a colouring cream once a week, as instructed by an advertisement in a Chinese magazine: 'Cover your grey with a simple application each day.'

The colour of my hair was now a dark shade of copper, and it was thin and shaggy. I had a permanent wave once every few months, to keep it short and manageable.

Like my father the farmer, I had lumps of bulging veins in my legs. They caused my feet to swell, and the puffiness made me itch, I couldn't help scratching. Ulcers appeared on my shin; they were my daily battle. I spent a whole hour before I slept, dressing and bandaging them. The tiny blue tablets the skin doctor prescribed made me drowsy, but night cramps interrupted my sleep; in the morning getting up was an effort, my joints stiff and numb. I walked reeling from side to side like a drunk.

Modern medicine — coloured capsules, sugar-coated tablets, tubes and jars of greasy ointment, creams, lotions — didn't seem to help. By now I'd lost faith in Western medicine. I turned to the traditional treatments: acupuncture and moxibustion. The faith and belief in a practice of many centuries was ingrained in me. I joined the tai chi class at the ACCA, and kept myself mobile, walking for long distance in Chinatown, and bush walking with Kim and Suchin on weekends.

I consulted a Chinese physician, Mr Zhou, a disciple of the Shao Lin Temple of Kung Fu and traditional Chinese healing. Mr Zhou was dressed like the herbalist-physician in my village of Lung Sun, in a Chinese tunic with buttons down the centre. In winter he wore a silk quilted jacket. He massaged my aching muscles, and manipulated my stiff joints. He also came from the province of Canton, and spoke Cantonese.

'How long have you been here?' he asked after he applied moxibustion on my stomach.

'Ten years or so.'

'Are you a citizen?'

I told him how I had managed to obtain my permament residency when Mr Whitlam was elected: 'There was an amnesty.'

'You're lucky to have been here at the right time. It's not easy now.' His wife came in, he was wanted on the phone.

Kim whispered: 'He married an Australian woman, in order to become an Australian citizen.'

He returned to remove the moxibustion cup from me, and continued the conversation: 'It's difficult now with the "points" system. Very costly. I've paid altogether thirty-five thousand dollars in cash to a "migrant consultant" to grant my son — from my first wife in China — a student who overstayed here, a permanent residency. He waited four years before he finally got it.'

He shook his head and sighed. 'My brothers and sisters also want to come. Better future and prospects here than in China. But now these consultants want a fifty thousand dollars up-front fee. Bribery is the only way to expedite the application.'

A few months later Kim told me that his wife — the one from China — had arrived, and had gone to the clinic to see her; she was pregnant.

'His baby?' I asked.

'He's a bigamist, by force of circumstances.'

Australia's two hundredth birth-year — 1988, the Year of the Dragon.

'It is an auspicious year,' I said. 'The Chinese like to give birth in the Year of the Dragon. People born under this birth sign are destined to be very important. It used to be an imperial sign, that of the emperor.'

The television news on New Year's eve showed the Prime Minister, Bob Hawke, announcing plans for a year-long celebration in all the states of Australia during the Bicentennial year.

The year whirled by. On the television I saw the happenings in Sydney and other states, events which swept me along dizzy and heady — tall ships sailing in the harbour, the Opera House bubbling with programs, concerts, symphony orchestra, children singing, flowers blooming, Aborigines dancing with their painted faces . . . Sydney vibrant with plays and rock music, the ghosts of the past resurrected in the enactment of Australia's history. Because Suchin was studying for the higher school certificate examinations, we couldn't attend the World Expo in Brisbane. But closer to home a whole new exciting complex was opened — the Darling Harbour, with its Chinese Gardens and a monorail. It was while queueing for a ride in the monorail that I saw May Ly and her family again. Before she entered her carriage she told me she had moved to Point Piper: 'Not far from your place in Potts Point.'

'She's stepped up in the world,' remarked Kim. 'Look at the trappings of wealth: Chanel suit and matching handbag, a Rolex solid gold watch and those diamond rings . . .'

'They were boat people ten years ago, dressed in Vincent de Paul shirts, jeans and sneakers, and always on the lookout for the cheapest cut of meat.'

'What does her husband do?'

'He's a clerk in the Immigration office.'

'People like him are on the receiving end of cash payments from Mr Zhou and thousands of desperate illegal immigrants, and become the new rich.'

'Is it a crime to accept bribes?'

Kim thought for a long time. 'Only as an evasion of income tax. There must be a whole lot of people involved, from the consultants outside to the connection inside the department, and the staff in the overseas embassies . . .'

'A whole can of worms.'

For me, the highlight of the celebrations were the fireworks set off from the Harbour Bridge, lighting up the whole expanse of dark sky like jewels, spreading, scattering, twinkling in intricate patterns — now an umbrella, a spray of roses, now a chrysanthemum, then a wattle — colours, lights, forms, dancing then dispersing into the darkness beyond. Flames of fire and light came alive in the black canvas of the sky.

Chinatown had now extended to Sussex Street. Dixon Street was a mall. The previous Wu Han restaurant had been rebuilt into a shopping arcade lined with new shops.

'It's like another CBD, modern and sophisticated,' Kim said. 'No longer the dingy dark alley filled with the clicking of mah-jong tiles and the restaurant serving the "long and short" soup.'

Another new goldsmith shop was opening, the fifth one in Chinatown, amidst the bang of firecrackers. Baskets of flowers with congratulatory notes written on red ribbons sat on the pavement outside the shop. I couldn't believe my eyes. Mrs Tran, in a floral shirt and black pants, appeared at the threshold to welcome the guests. She seemed awkward and slightly embarrassed on seeing me, but invited us in.

'Come and browse. It's forty percent discount for all items this week.' And she introduced Kim to one of her many daughters.

'Come and visit me and have lunch at my home one day,' she said.

'Still at the same place?' I asked her.

She nodded.

I thought: an owner of a goldsmith shop living in a government housing flat, still officially tagged with the status of a refugee.

Another 'refugee success' story.

Seeing is believing. Now are the days of simultaneous satellite transmission, you too can be an eye-witness to events happening anywhere in the world. You no longer need to depend on rumours and gossip, as in the days of old.

We watched with horror and disgust as the tanks crushed the protestors in Tiananmen Square. Fourth of June 1989. We too felt desperate and helpless as Bob Hawke cried publicly in Canberra amidst a crowd of Chinese students, condemning China's behaviour. And from this moment of nationwide compassion, thousands of Chinese students were granted an extension of four years' stay in Australia.

Bonnie was one such protestor against the Tiananmen massacre, carrying a banner in front of the Town Hall, and later burning the Chinese flag in front of the Chinese embassy in Elizabeth Street. She was from my village of Lung Sun, a distant relative of Lee Sao, also related remotely to Han. She called me 'Auntie Silver', an address of respect and courtesy. Bonnie, aged forty-two, had come to Australia as an English language student. She had borrowed money from the villagers for the trip. She was their investment. She remitted money home every month — the interest on the loan. 'They think that Australia is a goldmine,' she said.

Bonnie worked fourteen hours per day, doing two jobs. Nominally she was registered in a language school but had never attended class.

'I do two jobs, working in a clothing factory during the day, and waitressing in the evening. On weekends I work in a nursing home. My weekend pay is doubled. I net eight to nine hundred dollars per week.'

'Not bad,' I remarked.

'But I have no time to sleep. I doze off in the train or bus,' she continued. 'Jobs are harder to get. All Chinese students stranded here are looking for jobs, since the massacre their grant or scholarship have been suspended. They go from shop to shop soliciting for work. Some even work as prostitutes.'

Three months later she announced: 'I'm getting married.'

I attended the wedding as her Aunt Silver Wong, her only 'near kin.' It was a mass wedding. There were twenty couples, mainly Asians marrying Australians or Europeans, in the serene Japanese Gardens in Auburn. Bonnie wore a white wedding gown with a long train and a veil. Afterwards she posed for photos with her Vietnamese husband, Bill Huynh.

The master of ceremonies was an Asian lady, stout and bejewelled, with green eyeshadow. She gave a speech in English, Chinese and Vietnamese.

I was very impressed by her versatility of language.

I lost touch with Bonnie after her wedding. When we moved to a new flat in Kent Street, some eighteen months later, Kim sent her a card with our new address and telephone number.

She came to visit me. She was alone.

'How's your husband?' I asked her.

'I haven't seen him since the wedding. It was a sham marriage,' she explained. 'I paid eight thousand dollars to that Asian lady, and now I've permanent residency, with my wedding certificate.' She quickly added: 'Don't tell anyone, I'm waiting for a divorce.'

Bonnie worked hard, saved money. After her divorce she returned to Lung Sun for a visit to reassure her creditors that she was now a permanent resident in this rich country, and that their offshore investment in her would appreciate with time.

She told me Lee Sao had died from the shock of the Tiananmen massacre.

A new decade opens another door. Probably the last in this passage of my life before the final exit. Now my doors are glass with infra-red sensors. Automatic. These magic doors guard the entrance to where I live in Jones Street, Ultimo.

In March 1991, the secretary of the ACCA informs me that my request for accommodation in a new complex, specially designed for the senior citizens of the Chinese community, has been approved. I am allotted a one-bedroom unit on the ground floor, next to the caretaker. It has an en-suite shower, toilet and laundry, and a patio. Across the street is a row of terrace houses with iron-lace balconies. It takes me only twenty minutes to walk to Kim's home. I visit her at least once a week. Suchin is now studying at Sydney University, graduating at the end of this year in Commerce and Law.

At last I am settled in my own flat. With my old age pension, and my savings from a lifetime of working as an amah, I can now afford to take things easy, and live comfortably. I inherit a few pieces of furniture from Kim: a sofa bed, a dining-table with one broken leg, three foldaway chairs from Ikea, a futon, a fridge and a large colour television and video-recorder, both ten years old which still work. I tune in to the Cantonese news on the ethnic radio three times a week, and rent video tapes of soap operas from Hong Kong. It excites me to watch these epics, the same as those narrated by the storyteller in the one lit-up street in Lung Sun, now come alive in sound and colour on my television screen. I still cry, identifying with the fate and misfortunes of the heroine. On the Walkman Kim bought me I listen to the operatic arias which Little Peacock Lien used to sing in her concerts. Modern technology. The mementoes of my past packaged, condensed and stored in plastic, like the food in the supermarket. Preserved and ready for use.

I sit back in my chair with my feet up, eyes closed. I finger the smooth pebble on the gold chain round my neck and dream of my past.

I think of all the people I have known in my long life, so many diverse characters from different backgrounds. The strong and weak, cunning and deceitful, honest and courageous. And I wonder if there is a deity that guides our destiny and designs our fate and metes out justice. Ah Han and myself, the two survivors of our sisterhood, are living thousands of miles apart.

Ah Han wrote recently: 'I've been converted to a charismatic Christian, and my new church friends are very caring and dependable. They have helped me settle in an old folks' home, and I've obtained an old age pension, a small sum, but sufficient.'

Her church friends are closer to her by physical proximity than me, her 'comb-up' sister. This lessens my responsibility towards her. In her letters she often mentions the kindness of her 'brothers' and 'sisters' in Christ.

I see flags of many colours flying in the wind, hoisted high up along the Pyrmont Bridge, Dixon Street Mall, George Street, in front of the Town Hall . . . All feature a large M, its tail curled up slightly. The arms of the two Ms are in blue, black, red, yellow and green. My neighbour Mrs Chin tells me that Sydney has won the bid for the Olympics 2000. I shed a tear and my chest heaves with pride as I watch the people of Sydney become hilarious with joy at the announcement, and the fantastic display of fireworks which follows.

'It's another seven years before the Games take place in Sydney,' Kim reminds me. 'You'll be eighty-nine years old then.'

'I bet you I'll still be around,' I reply. 'And I'll be watching it all on TV, especially the opening and closing ceremonies. I watched those at the Barcelona Olympics, and I'm confident Sydney's will be just as impressive. And I'm sure our local athletes will win many, many gold medals for the glory of my adopted country.'

GLOSSARY

aiyah lai ren ah	oh dear somebody please come
aiyah nee lai ler	oh you've come
ay-ni-to-fa	form of greeting to Buddhist monk or nun
bad-winds	complications of an illness, puerperal fever
bomoh	witch doctor
chi-chak	wall lizard
feng kwei	foreign or wild devils, barbarians
feng shui	wind and water. The siting of a place; a good atmosphere ensures prosperity for the family or later generations
foo	an amulet or charm of protection
hai hai	yes, yes (Japanese)
han-ji	ideogram or Chinese words, used by Japanese
ikan nasi	fish and rice (Malay)
kelong	fishing station
koniens	ladies, women

li	half a mile, or 0.31 km
loc or six	puns with good fortune
lohans	people who have achieved Nirvana, usually depicted in groupings of 8, 16, 18 and 200.
moshi moshi	hello in Japanese as used on the phone
'one leg kick'	an amah who does general work, washing, cleaning, cooking, marketing, ironing, etc
pasa-malam	night market
putehs	the whites, Europeans (Malay)
ren lai lah	somebody's approaching
sai	small
sam-foo	tunic and pant suit worn by Chinese
siasin-loa	a person who reads and writes letters, for a fee
stengah	half and half, whisky and water
tai	big or number one
tai-sai	big and small, a game of dice also known as *feng*
tung	
tai tai	polite form of addressing the mistress
teachers	polite form of address for males
tongkans	rice barges
tong kwei . . .	a tonic found in roots, as ginseng
towkay	head of the family, boss
Yellow Springs	hell
yi	number two